THE MARIA T[...] BIODYNAMIC [...]ENDAR

2015

The original biodynamic sowing and planting calendar
showing the optimum days for sowing, pruning and harvesting
various plant-crops, as well as for beekeeping

Created by
Maria and Matthias Thun

Floris Books

Compiled by Matthias Thun
and Christina Schmidt Rüdt
Translated by Bernard Jarman
Additional astronomical material
by Wolfgang Held and Christian Maclean

Published in German under the title *Aussaattage*
English edition published by Floris Books

MIX
Paper from
responsible sources
FSC
www.fsc.org
FSC® C117931

British Library CIP Data available

ISBN 978-178250-106-0
ISSN: 2052-5761

Printed in Great Britain
by MBM Print Solutions, Glasgow

Walter Thun, Landscape near Blassenburg, Thuringia, *water colour, 1939, 48 × 65 cm*

Landscape near Blassenburg, Thuringia

Looking at this image, we can see how Walter Thun as an artist opened his whole heart to his native landscape of Thuringia. As children we could experience his enthusiasm when, at bedtime, he told us tales from Thuringia. He had walked through the length and breadth of the land with his father, and knew every nook and corner of Thuringia.

This picture shows the rye fields in a wealth of colours, and trees manifesting different forms and shades. The landscape includes the hamlets and villages in the valleys.

When Walter Thun came to neighbouring Hesse in 1945, he got to know it with eagerness, finding similarities with his native landscapes. This helped him settle in Hesse with his wife Maria. His love of the landscapes of Thuringia and Hesse remained with him to the end of his life.

Introduction

In this 2015 Calendar we would like to focus on questions that readers have frequently asked us. We will therefore be addressing the special qualities of rye, from sowing the seed to baking the bread.

Since gardeners and farmers suffer not only from the depredations of slugs and snails but also Colorado beetles, ways to control them using insect peppers are also discussed.

Then there is the recurring question as to why soil and plants should be left in peace on Good Friday and Easter Saturday.

Readers of the Calendar in Slovenia have shared their experiences, and we would like to thank them warmly for their contributions.

Of course there is the monthly calendar and the recommendations that accompany it. We hope you will enjoy reading the 2015 Calendar, and that it makes your work with the soil, plants and bees easier.

In the course of the year there are four seasons. In winter there is a kind of immobility and life comes almost to a standstill. In spring nature wakes up and a new joyous period of growth begins. The summer is about fruit development. Autumn brings fruiting processes to completion but also, in the case of winter cereals, rape and other crops that require the winter for healthy growth, it pre-empts the spring. These crops experience a kind of temporary pause that enables them to grow quicker when the real spring arrives. They can then grow rapidly and reach maturity in early summer – important in situations where this is needed or wished for.

For farmers and gardeners, autumn is therefore a kind of pre-spring period. Harvest is complete, crops are stored away and the land can be cultivated in readiness for future crops. The ground is treated with manure or compost or perhaps sown with a green manure crop. Preparation for next year's growing period is beginning.

Wintertime, which in many parts of the world is cold with snow and ice and in other regions is dry and barren, provides an opportunity to reflect on one's work with the soil, plants, animals and fellow human beings and consider future steps.

This means seeking answers to questions that have arisen during the course of the year. The questions requiring answers are often those that relate to life, the nature of life or the living world in general.

The autumn of 2013 was very wet in our part of the world, but arable crops like cereals, rape and potatoes could be more or less successfully harvested. A lot of straw and later cuts of hay, however, were spoiled and winter cereals had to be sown in soil that was too wet.

For backyard gardeners this was not such a problem since they could always ready their small plots for the winter between rainy periods.

For beekeepers and bees there was a limited amount of pollen available. They

4

so looked forward to a proper winter with now and frost, for then there would be pause in the raising of brood and the 1reat from the varroa mite would be 1ssened.

The winter that everyone had hoped or did not materialise, however. Here the otal snowfall of the winter amounted to ttle more than 30 cm (12 in). Each time ; fell, it was gone a few hours later.

After a wet autumn and warm winter, ould the coming of spring be wet and old or warm and dry?

The spring was wonderful, the soil etained sufficient winter moisture to llow strong growth. It only rained occa- ionally and this allowed farmers and gar- leners to start cultivating their soil and owing seeds much earlier than usual. It 1as a pure 'picture book' spring. Beekeep- rs and their colonies were content. Bees ound a rich supply of pollen and nectar. They grew rapidly and produced an excel- ent crop of honey from the fruit orchards 1nd dandelions. In my fifty years of keep- ng bees I have never experienced such an arly and heavy yield of honey. Because of his strong colony growth there was also a oowerful swarming drive that resulted in really large swarms.

The beautiful spring led into a period of very changeable weather. There was 1 very dry spell followed by high winds, storms and heavy rain. These extreme conditions showed, however, which varie- ties of rape and barley were best able to cope with such changeable weather. Some varieties of rape, though not yet ripe enough to harvest, had already opened their pods and released their seeds. Cer- tain varieties of barley had stems which snapped during a normal thunder storm. Was this due to the variety or was it caused by a fungus attack? Other varie- ties of rape and barley stood up well and could be harvested in the normal way.

Only once before do I remember a similar snapping of barley stems, and that was during the 1970s or 80s and it was not as pronounced as this. In her cereal trials Maria Thun had planted two new varieties. They were varieties of naked barley and naked oats that had been bred to produce husk-less grain. It meant, however, that the halms were very weak and compromised the plants' stabil- ity. Yields were also 30% below those of the normal varieties with husks. Neither of these varieties were therefore suitable for further cultivation. The breaking of stems and tendency for lodging can be addressed by applying biodynamic horn silica preparation. It is applied in the afternoon at Root times when the stem is already formed and the cereal is starting to shoot. It brings about greater elasticity and firmness in the halms.

Biodynamic barley with unbroken halms after a thunderstorm

Rye

Rye is one of the oldest grains. It was always planted in places where the soil was poor in nutrients. These were generally soils with a low clay content, the so-called poor and lighter soils in sandstone regions or, as is the case with us in Dexbach, shale soils. Until the 1970s rye was the primary grain for bread baking on lighter soils. In upland areas, especially in southern Germany, spelt was often planted as an alternative to rye on land that was not suitable for wheat. With the advent of artificial fertiliser use in agriculture, the growing of rye declined. The old varieties couldn't cope with it. They grew strongly but their long stems and heavy ears could not withstand the buffeting of storms and this resulted in extensive lodging and made the late harvest especially difficult.

Around this time consumer tastes were also changing. Wheat, once considered a luxury, now began to replace rye. It is sweeter, there is less variation in flavour than with sour dough bread, it is lighter, less filling and more enjoyable to eat and so rye was gradually replaced by wheat.

As with spelt, there were old wheat varieties that grew particularly well on lighter soils. The traditional land race wheat from Hessen is worth mentioning at this point. It could almost be considered as a wheat relative of the old long straw rye. It was planted as late as the 1960s in areas where conditions were unsuited to the more demanding wheat varieties.

The Hessen land race wheat is a lon strawed and bearded wheat. It is stron growing, undemanding and has a ver good baking quality. Its straw, like that c rye, is very firm and elastic so long as it i not over-fertilised. As with rye, an after noon application of horn silica at Roo times during the period of halm develop ment (between 30–40 cm, 12–16 in, tall) helps to increase wind resistance. How ever, the treatment should not be given once the ears have started to emerge from among the leaves. It is then too late and would harm ear development.

In the early years of biodynamic agri culture there was as yet little knowledge of how to use the horn silica prepara tion. It was applied out of a feeling for what was needed and very little was known about its effects on plants. It was, for example, sometimes applied in order to deal with pest or fungal problems or enhance fruit ripening. As time went by these ideas were found to be incorrect. Only later, from about the mid-1950s, were specific trials undertaken to gain more understanding of it.

The silica preparation is sprayed at very particular moments in a plant's development. This moment varies from plant to plant. Applications should be made three times in succession at roughly nine-day intervals. The influence of the Moon constellations relating to Fruit, Root, Flower and Leaf types repeat themselves every nine days or so. Leaf plants such as lettuce and spinach are, for example, treated

ye at the two-leaf stage

Mature rye

ith the preparation at three successive
eaf times; that is, when the Moon is in
corpio, Pisces and Cancer.

Cereals, as well as tomatoes and
ucumbers, are treated at three succes-
ive Fruit times with the Moon in Sagit-
arius, Aries and Leo.

The first spraying of horn silica is car-
ied out on cereals when the plants are at
he two-leaf stage. Then at a Fruit time
he first spray is given followed nine days
ater by a second and after a further nine
lays, a third spray. During this time the
lants will start to tiller.

Horn silica is sprayed this early in order
o support the already developing ears at
he two-leaf stage. This in turn leads to
mproved quality and higher yields.

In some situations, especially in moun-
ainous regions, the ripening of cereals
s often delayed. An application of horn
ilica is then frequently recommended in
rder to speed up ripening. Experience,
lowever, shows this to be a mistake.

Horn silica always serves to enhance
growth and vitality. But when cereals
ipen, a de-vitalising process is at work
nd this is necessary to improve quality.

If horn silica is applied during this time
when the rye is extremely sensitive, the de-
vitalising/ripening process will be stopped
and a new growth impulse encouraged. If
then a prolonged rainy period comes, the
grains of nearly ripened corn will start to
sprout and render the crop useful only as
animal feed and not for baking.

The horn silica preparation is therefore not a 'cure all' but should only be
applied in order to encourage vitality and
growth.

This description indicates how sensitive a plant can be. However robust the
rye may appear it is easily affected by
careless management.

The cultivation of rye begins with its sowing. It should be drilled at Fruit times. If
seed corn is the aim, a time with the Moon
in Leo should be chosen, although a strong
growth of weeds is also likely since a Leo
cultivation encourages more weed seeds to
germinate. More work with the hoe and
harrow may then become necessary.

The best days for producing grain for
bread baking are when the Moon is in
Sagittarius. Fewer weeds are encouraged

7

at this time and less weed control will be needed.

Should it not be possible to sow at a Fruit time, a Root time can be chosen for rye (but not for other cereals). Subsequent harrowing and silica applications should then be carried out at Fruit times.

To grow really good quality rye it is important to consider the soil and also other planetary aspects. In this Calendar it is recommended that planetary occultations are avoided. When an occultation occurs the planet hidden behind the Moon cannot exert its influence. If growth is to be healthy all planets must be effective otherwise weaknesses will arise.

Occultations lead to weakened and damaged growth. If rye is sown during an occultation not only is there likely to be a disturbance in its growth pattern, it may also lead to ergot infection. If wheat is sown during an occultation there is a high chance of it contracting rust – another fungus disease.

A particular problem occurs when a good sowing time has been chosen, the grain is ready to bring in and there is an eclipse or an occultation while it is being harvested. This will affect the seeds sown for the next season's crop and beyond, and produce weak and sickly plants. In such situations treatments with herbal teas will be of no help since the cause lies in the seed stock and not in the fungus spores carried by wind and rain.

The soil can also bring about a strengthening or weakening. It has already been mentioned how undemanding the rye is. Biodynamic practice seeks to encourage a diversity of living substances to thrive

in the soil so that the plant itself can fin what it needs for growth. Over-rich fert lisation with fresh manure is therefore t be avoided in preference to ripe one-yea old compost. This largely prevents pes and disease problems.

Farmers often turn their noses u when it comes to horse manure. Hors manure compost has, however, bee found to produce the best quality oat Cow manure compost is also improved b the addition of a tenth part horse manure It brings warmth which in turn encou ages more fungal activity. Colonisation b the small ink cap fungus marks the star of the process and the arrival of manur worms its conclusion. Ink caps don't lik excessive wind.

Rye grows well on land treated wit such compost. However, it dislikes grow ing in rich half-ripe manure or plan compost. It then becomes susceptible t fungal problems in storage and can lea to ergot infection.

If farmers succeed in providing th right conditions for the rye crop, they wil have the best foundation for producin good and wholesome rye bread.

Baking bread with rye, however, is not a simple as with wheat. Just as it is sensi tive to its growing conditions, rye is als demanding when it comes to being mad into bread if it is to unfold its full poten tial within the human organism.

Large bakeries are rarely able t undertake what seems on the face of it t be a very labour-intensive procedure. The usually add a certain amount of whea flour to the mix along with some yeast t

Ergot on rye

Treatment with horn silica preparation at Root times to improve wind resistance of halms. From right: wheat, barley, oats

Rye planted on a fresh embankment

help it rise, rather than using a genuine sour dough.

The recipe on page 45 may seem very complicated. But don't give up on it. It is actually quite simple and straightforward once it has been done a few times.

While rye is grown for its grain and to bake bread, the straw is used in the cattle shed, and also by beekeepers who want to make a hive with straw. These skeps (baskets) are best made using rye straw. Our tests showed that bees gnaw away at barley and oat straw. Loam used in post and beam construction was combined with chopped rye straw. This not only prolonged its life but helped insulation.

Another, quite different use for rye is in road building. New cuttings and embankments need to be made safe so the earth is not washed away in the next heavy shower. Rye has deep, tough roots and has little need for manuring; it can grow quickly in the poor soils of fresh landscaping and hold the topsoil until wild plants take root. Even today rye is still used for this at some difficult sites.

Background to the calendar

The zodiac

The **zodiac** is a group of twelve constellations of stars which the Sun, Moon and all the planets pass on their circuits. The Sun's annual path always takes exactly the same line, called **ecliptic.** The Moon's and planets' paths vary slightly, sometimes above and sometimes below the ecliptic. The point at which their paths cross the ecliptic is called a **node** (☊ and ☋).

The angles between the Sun, Moon and planets are called **aspects.** In this calendar the most important is the 120° angle, or **trine.**

In this illustration the outer circle shows the varying sizes of the visible **constellations** of the **zodiac.** The dates on this outer circle are the days on which the Sun enters the constellation (this can change by one day because of leap years). The inner circle shows the divisions into equal sections of 30° corresponding to the **signs** used in astrology.

It is the constellations on which our observations are based, and which are used throughout this calendar.

The twelve constellations are grouped into four different types, each having three constellations at an angle of about 120°, or trine. About every nine days the Moon passes from one type, for instance Root, through the other types (Flower Leaf and Fruit) and back to Root again.

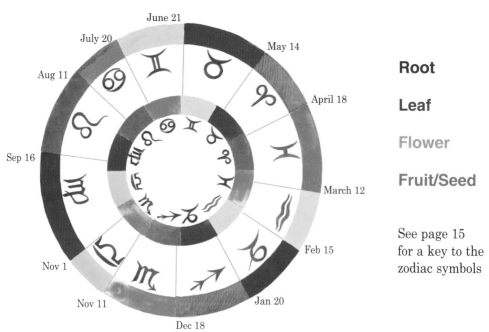

Root

Leaf

Flower

Fruit/Seed

See page 15 for a key to the zodiac symbols

If a New Moon is at a node there is solar eclipse, as the Moon is directly ı front of the Sun, while a Full Moon t a node causes a lunar eclipse where ıe Earth's shadow falls on the Moon. If ıe Sun or Moon pass exactly in front of planet, there is an occultation (•). If Iercury or Venus pass exactly in front of ıe Sun, this is a transit (other planets ınnot pass in front of the Sun).

Trines △ or ▲

The twelve constellations are grouped into four different types, each having three constellations at an angle of about 120°, or trine. About every nine days the Moon passes a similar region of forces.

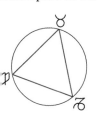

Earth-Root

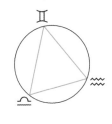

Light-Flower

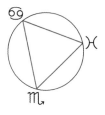

Water-Leaf

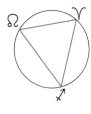

Warmth-Fruit/Seed

Vhat are oppositions, trines and conjunctions?

)ppositions ☍

. *geocentric* (Earth-centred) opposition ccurs when for the observer on the Earth here are two planets opposite one another – 180° apart — in the heavens. They look t one another from opposite sides of the ky and their light interpenetrates. Their ays fall on to the Earth and stimulate in beneficial way the seeds that are being own in that moment. In our trials we ave found that seeds sown at times of pposition resulted in a higher yield of top uality crops.

With a *heliocentric* (Sun-centred) opp-sition an observer would need to place hemselves on the Sun. This is of course

physically impossible but we can under-stand it through our thinking. The Sun is in the centre and the two planets placed 180° apart also gaze at each other but this time across the circle of the Sun's orbit. Their rays are also felt by the Earth and stimulate better plant growth. However, heliocentric oppositions are not shown in the calendar.

At times of opposition two zodiac constellations are also playing their part. If one planet is standing in a Warmth constellation, the second one will usually be in a Light constellation or vice versa. If one planet is in a Water constellation, the other will usually be in an Earth one. (As the constellations are not equally sized, the point opposite may not always be in the opposite constellation.)

Trines △ or ▲

Trines occur when planets are 120° from one another. The two planets are then usually both standing in the same elemental configuration – Aries and Leo for example are both Warmth constellations. A Warmth trine means that the effects of these constellations will enhance fruit and seed formation in the plants sown at this time. If two planets are in trine position in Water, watery influences will be enhanced which usually brings high rainfall. Plants sown on these days will yield more leaf than those on other days. Trine effects can change the way plants grow.

Conjunctions ☌

Conjunctions and multiple conjunctions occur when two or more planets stand behind one another in space. It is then usually only the planet closest to the Earth that has any influence on plant growth. If this influence is stronger than that of the sidereal Moon, cosmic disturbances can occur that irritate the plant and cause checks in growth. This negative effect is increased further when the Moon or another planet stands directly in front of another – an occultation (☌) or eclipse in the case of Sun and Moon. Sowing at these times will affect subsequent growth detrimentally and harm a plant's regenerative power.

The effects of the Moon

In its 27-day orbit round the Earth th Moon passes through the constellation of the zodiac and transmits forces to th Earth which affect the four element: Earth, Light (Air), Water and Warmt (Fire). They in turn affect the four parts the plant: the roots, the flower, the leave and the fruit or seeds. The health an growth of a plant can therefore be stimu lated by sowing, cultivating and harvestin it in tune with the cycles of the Moon.

These cosmic forces can also be har nessed in beekeeping. By opening and clos ing the bee 'skep' or box in rhythm wit the Moon, the bees' activity can be directl affected.

The table opposite summarizes th effects of the movement of the Moo through the twelve constellations o plants, bees and the weather.

The amount of time the Moon spends i any constellation varies between two an four days. However, this basic framewor can be disrupted by planetary opposition which override the normal tendencies equally, it may be that trine position (see above) activate a different elementa force to the ones the Moon is transmitting Times when the Moon's path or a planet' path intersects with the ecliptic (ascend ing ☊ or descending ☋ node; see previ ous page) are subject to mainly negativ effects. These are intensified if there is a eclipse or occultation, in which case th nearer planet interrupts the influence o the distant one. Such days are unsuitabl for sowing or harvesting.

Constellation	Sign		Element	Weather	Plant	Bees
Pisces, Fishes	♓	W	Water	Damp	Leaf	Making honey
Aries, Ram	♈	H	Warmth	Warm/hot	Fruit	Gathering nectar
Taurus, Bull	♉	E	Earth	Cool/cold	Root	Building comb
Gemini, Twins	♊	L	Light	Airy/bright	Flower	Gathering pollen
Cancer, Crab	♋	W	Water	Damp	Leaf	Making honey
Leo, Lion	♌	H	Warmth	Warm/hot	Fruit	Gathering nectar
Virgo, Virgin	♍	E	Earth	Cool/cold	Root	Building comb
Libra, Scales	♎	L	Light	Airy/bright	Flower	Gathering pollen
Scorpio, Scorpion	♏	W	Water	Damp	Leaf	Making honey
Sagittarius, Archer	♐	H	Warmth	Warm/hot	Fruit	Gathering nectar
Capricorn, Goat	♑	E	Earth	Cool/cold	Root	Building comb
Aquarius, Waterman	♒	L	Light	Airy/bright	Flower	Gathering pollen

Groupings of plants for sowing and harvesting

When we grow plants, different parts are cultivated for food. We can divide them into four groups.

Root crops at Root times

Radishes, swedes, sugar beet, beetroot, celeriac, carrot, scorzonera, etc. fall into the category of root plants. Potatoes and onions are included in this group too. Root times produce good yields and top storage quality for these crops.

Leaf plants at Leaf times

The cabbage family, lettuce, spinach, lambs lettuce, endive, parsley, leafy herbs and fodder plants are categorized as leaf plants. Leaf days are suitable for sowing and tending these plants but not for harvesting and storage. For this (as well as harvesting of cabbage for sauerkraut) Fruit and Flower times are recommended.

Flower plants at Flower times

These times are favourable for sowing and tending all kinds of flower plants but also for cultivating and spraying 501 (a biodynamic preparation) on oil-bearing plants such as linseed, rape, sunflower, etc. Cut flowers have the strongest scent and remain fresh for longer if cut at Flower times, and the mother plant will provide many new side shoots. If flowers for drying are harvested at Flower times they retain the most vivid colours. If cut at other times they soon lose their colour. Oil-bearing plants are best harvested at Flower times.

Fruit Plants at Fruit times

Plants which are cultivated for their fruit or seed belong to this category, including beans, peas, lentils, soya, maize, tomatoes, cucumber, pumpkin, courgettes, but also cereals for summer and winter crops.

Sowing oil-bearing plants at Fruit times provides the best yields of seeds. The best time for extraction of oil later on is at Flower times. Leo times are particularly suitable to grow good seed. Fruit plants are best harvested at Fruit times. They store well and their seeds provide good plants for next year. When storing fruit, also remember to choose the time of the ascending Moon.

There is always uncertainty as to whic category some plants belong. Onions an beetroot provide a similar yield when sow at Root and Leaf times, but the keepin quality is best from Root times. Kohlral and cauliflowers belong to Leaf time: as does Florence fennel. Broccoli is mor beautiful and firmer when sown at Flowe times.

Explanations of the calendar pages

Next to the date is the constellation (and time of entry) in which the Moon is. This is the astronomical constellation, not the astrological sign (see page 10). The next column shows solar and lunar events.

A further column shows which element is dominant on that day (this is useful for beekeepers). Note **H** is used for warmth (heat). Sometimes there is a change during the day; in this case, both elements are mentioned. Warmth effects on thundery days are implied but are not mentioned in this column, but may have a ♄ symbol in the far right 'Weather' column.

The next column shows in colour the part of the plant which will be enhanced by sowing or cultivation on that day. Numbers indicate times of day. On the extreme right, special events in nature are noted as well as anticipated weather changes which disturb or break up the overall weather pattern.

When parts of the plant are indicated that do not correspond to the Moon's position in the zodiac (often it is more than one part on the same day), it is not a mis-

print, but takes account of other cosmi aspects which overrule the Moon-zodia pattern and have an effect on a differen part of the plant.

Unfavourable times are marked thu: (- - -). These are caused by eclipses, noda points of the Moon or the planets or othei aspects with a negative influence; they are not elaborated in the calendar. If one has to sow at unfavourable times for practica' reasons, one can choose favourable days for hoeing, which will improve the plant.

The position of the planets in the zodiac is shown in the box below, with the date of entry into a new constellation. R indicates the planet is moving retrograde (with the date when retrograde begins), D indicates the date when it moves in direct. motion again.

On the opposite calendar page astronomical aspects are indicated. Those visible to the naked eye are shown in **bold** type. Visible conjunctions (particularly Mercury's) are not always visible from all parts of the Earth.

Astronomical symbols

Constellations	Planets	Aspects		
♓ Pisces	☉ Sun	☊ Ascending node	St	Storms likely
♈ Aries	☾,☽ Moon	☋ Descending node	♄	Thunder likely
♉ Taurus	☿ Mercury	⌒ Highest Moon	Eq	Earthquakes
♊ Gemini	♀ Venus	⌄ Lowest Moon	Tr	Traffic dangers
♋ Cancer	♂ Mars	Pg Perigee	Vo	Volcanic activity
♌ Leo	♃ Jupiter	Ag Apogee		Northern Trans-
♍ Virgo	♄ Saturn	☍ Opposition		planting Time
♎ Libra	♅ Uranus	☌ Conjunction		
♏ Scorpio	♆ Neptune	✦ Eclipse/occultation		Southern Trans-
♐ Sagittarius	♇ Pluto	✦ Lunar eclipse		planting Time
♑ Capricorn	○ Full Moon	△ Trine (or ▲)		
♒ Aquarius	● New Moon	E Earth　L Light/Air　W Water　H Warmth/Heat		

Transplanting times

From midwinter through to midsummer the Sun rises earlier and sets later each day while its path across the sky ascends higher and higher. From midsummer until midwinter this is reversed, the days get shorter and the midday Sun shines from an ever lower point in the sky. This annual ascending and descending of the Sun creates our seasons. As it ascends and descends during the course of the year the Sun is slowly moving (from an Earth-centred point of view) through each of the twelve constellations of the zodiac in turn. On average it shines for one month from each constellation.

In the northern hemisphere the winter solstice occurs when the Sun is in the constellation of Sagittarius and the summer solstice when it is in Gemini. At any point from Sagittarius to Gemini the Sun is ascending, while from Gemini to Sagittarius it is descending. In the southern hemisphere this is reversed.

The Moon (and all the planets) follow approximately the same path as the Sun around the zodiac but instead of a year, the Moon takes only about 27½ days to complete one cycle, shining from each constellation in turn for a period of two to three days. This means that the Moon will ascend for about fourteen days and then descend.

It is important to distinguish the journey of the Moon through the zodiac (siderial rhythm) from the waxing and waning (synodic) cycle: in any given constellation

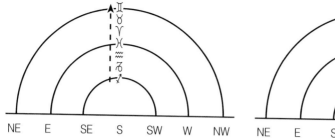 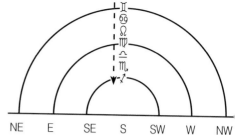

Northern hemisphere ascending Moon (left) and descending Moon (right): Transplanting Time

there may be a waxing, waning, full, quarter, sickle or gibbous Moon. As it moves through the zodiac the Moon, like the Sun, is ascending (in the northern hemisphere) when it is in the constellations from Sagittarius to Gemini and descending from Gemini to Sagittarius. In the southern hemisphere it is ascending from Gemini to Sagittarius and descending from Sagittarius to Gemini.

When the Moon is ascending, plant sap rises more strongly. The upper part of the plant fills with sap and vitality. This is a good time for cutting scions (for grafting). Fruit harvested during this period remains fresh for longer when stored.

When the Moon is descending, plants take root readily and connect well with their new location. This period is referred to as the **Transplanting Time.** Moving plants from one location to another is called *transplanting.* This is the case when young plants are moved from the seed bed into their final growing position but also when the gardener wishes to strengthen the root development of young fruit trees, shrubs or pot plants by frequently re-potting them. Sap movement is slower during the descending Moon. This is why it is a good time for trimming hedges, pruning trees and felling timber as well as applying compost to meadows, pastures and orchards.

Note that sowing is the moment when a seed is put into the soil; either the ascending or descending period can be used. It then needs time to germinate and grow. This is different from *transplanting* which is best done during the descending Moon. These times given in the calendar. Northern Transplanting Times refer to the northern hemisphere, and **Southern Transplanting Times** refer to the southern hemisphere. All other constellations and planetary aspects are equally valid in both hemispheres.

ocal times

mes given are *Greenwich Mean Time*
(MT), using 24-hour clock with ^{h} after
e time. Thus 15^h is 3 pm. **No account**
taken of daylight saving (summer)
me (DST). Note 0^h is midnight at the
•ginning of a date, and 24^h is midnight
the end of the date.
djust as follows for different countries:

urope

ritain, Ireland, Portugal, Iceland: GMT
  (DST from March 29 to Oct 24, add 1^h)
entral Europe: add 1^h
  (DST from March 29 to Oct 24, add 2^h)
astern Europe (Finland, etc.): add 2^h
  (DST from March 29 to Oct 24, add 3^h)
ussia (Moscow), Georgia: add 4^h (no DST)

frica/Asia

amibia: add 1^h
  (DST to April 4 & from Sep 6, add 2^h)
outh Africa, Egypt: add 2^h (no DST)
enya: add 3^h (no DST)
srael: add 2^h
  (DST from March 27 to Oct 24, add 3^h)
akistan: add 5^h (no DST)
ndia: add $5\frac{1}{2}^h$ (no DST)
angladesh: add 6^h (no DST)
hilippines, China: add 8^h (no DST)
apan: add 9^h (no DST)

ustralia/New Zealand

Western Australia: add 8^h (no DST)
outh Australia: add $9\frac{1}{2}^h$ (DST to
  April 4 & from Oct 4, add $10\frac{1}{2}^h$)
Northern Territory: add $9\frac{1}{2}^h$ (no DST)

Queensland: add 10^h (no DST)
ACT, NSW, Victoria, Tasmania: add 10^h
  (DST to April 4 & from Oct 4, add 11^h)
New Zealand: add 12^h (DST to April 4 and
  from Sep 27, add 13^h)

North America

Newfoundland Standard Time: subtract $3\frac{1}{2}^h$
  (DST March 8 to Oct 31, subtract $2\frac{1}{2}^h$)
Atlantic Standard Time: subtract 4^h
  (DST March 8 to Oct 31, subtract 3^h)
Eastern Standard Time: subtract 5^h
  (DST, March 8 to Oct 31, subtract 4^h)
Central Standard Time: subtract 6^h
  (DST, except Saskatchewan March 8 to
  Oct 31, subtract 5^h)
Mountain Standard Time: subtract 7^h
  (DST, except AZ, March 8 to Oct 31,
  subtract 6^h)
Pacific Standard Time: subtract 8^h
  (DST March 8 to Oct 31, subtract 7^h)
Alaska Standard Time: subtract 9^h
  (DST March 8 to Oct 31, subtract 8^h)
Hawaii Standard Time: subtract 10^h (no
  DST)
Mexico (mostly CST): subtract 6^h
  (DST, April 5 to Oct 24, subtract 5^h)

South America

Argentina: subtract 3^h (no DST)
Brazil (Eastern): subtract 3^h (DST to Feb
  21 and from Oct 18, subtract 2^h)
Chile: subtract 4^h (DST to March 14 and
  from Oct 11, subtract 3^h)
Columbia, Peru: subtract 5^h (no DST)

January 2015

All times in C

Date	Const. of Moon	Solar & lunar aspects	Moon Trines	Parts of the plant El'ment	Parts of the plant enhanced by Moon or planets 0 1 2 3 4 5 6 7 8 9 10 11 12 13 14 15 16 17 18 19 20 21 22 23 24	Weath
1 Thu	♉	6ʰ ☉-♐		H/E	Fruit to 5ʰ Root from 6ʰ	
2 Fri	♉			E	Root	
3 Sat	♉	♋ 18ʰ		E	Root to 24ʰ	St Eq V
4 Sun	♊	1ʰ		L	Flower from 1ʰ	St Eq Vo T
5 Mon	♊	○ 5ʰ		L	Flower	♄ T
6 Tue	♋	7ʰ		L/W	Flower to 6ʰ Leaf from 7ʰ	S
7 Wed	♋			W	Leaf to 23ʰ	S
8 Thu	♌	0ʰ		H	Fruit from 0ʰ	E
9 Fri	♌	Ag 18ʰ		H	Fruit	S
10 Sat	♍	23ʰ		H/E	Fruit to 22ʰ 23	St V
11 Sun	♍			E	Root	St E
12 Mon	♍	♌ 16ʰ		E	Root to 12ʰ - - - - - - - - Root 19ʰ	
13 Tue	♍	☾ 10ʰ		E	Root	
14 Wed	♎	19ʰ		E/L	Root to 18ʰ Flower 19ʰ	T
15 Thu	♎			L	Flower	St T
16 Fri	♏	4ʰ		L/W	Fl -3ʰ - - - - - - - - - - - - - - - - - -	
17 Sat	♏	☿ ♌		W	- - - - - - - - - - - - - - - - Leaf from 17ʰ	
18 Sun	♐	10ʰ ☌ 6ʰ		W/H	Leaf to 9ʰ Fruit from 10ʰ	
19 Mon	♐	☉-♑		H	Fruit	St Vo
20 Tue	♑	11ʰ ● 13ʰ		H/E	Fruit to 10ʰ Root from 11ʰ	
21 Wed	♑	Pg 20ʰ		E	Root to 8ʰ - - - - - - - - - - - - - - - - - -	St Eq T
22 Thu	♒	8ʰ		E/L	- - - - - - - - - - Flower from 9ʰ	
23 Fri	♒			L	Flower to 23ʰ	
24 Sat	♓	0ʰ		W	Leaf from 0ʰ	
25 Sun	♓	☋ 10ʰ ●☊		W	Leaf to 7ʰ - - - - - - - - Leaf from 14ʰ	
26 Mon	♈	16ʰ		W/H	Leaf to 15ʰ Fruit from 16ʰ	St Eq Vo T
27 Tue	♈	☽ 5ʰ		H	Fruit	V
28 Wed	♉	11ʰ		H/E	Fruit to 10ʰ Root from 11ʰ	
29 Thu	♉			E	Root	Vo
30 Fri	♉			E	Root	S
31 Sat	♊	7ʰ ♋ 1ʰ		E/L	Root to 6ʰ Flower from 7ʰ	S

0 1 2 3 4 5 6 7 8 9 10 11 12 13 14 15 16 17 18 19 20 21 22 23 24

Northern Transplanting Time

Southern Transplanting Time

Mercury ☿	Venus ♀	Mars ♂	Jupiter ♃	Saturn ♄	Uranus ♅	Neptune ♆	Pluto ♇
♐ 4 ♑	♐ 2 ♑	♑	♌ 29 ♋	♏	♓	♒	♐
(21 R)	24 ♒	8 ♒	(R)				

NB: All zodiac symbols refer to astronomical constellations, not astrological signs (see p.10

anetary aspects
  (Bold = *visible to naked eye*)

☽☌♄ 19ʰ ♂☍♃ 20ʰ

☉☌♇ 23ʰ

☽☍♇ 3ʰ
☾☌☿ 16ʰ ☾☌♀ 19ʰ

☾☌♃ 5ʰ ☾☍♂ 17ʰ
☾☍♆ 10ʰ

☾☍☉ 14ʰ

☾☌♄ 12ʰ
☿☋ 6ʰ

☾☌♇ 11ʰ ♀☍♃ 14ʰ
♂☌♆ 0ʰ
☽☌☿ 16ʰ ☽☍♃ 20ʰ
☽☌♀ 2ʰ ☽☍♆ 22ʰ
☽☌♂ 2ʰ

☽•☉ 11ʰ

☽☌♄ 5ʰ
☉☌☿ 14ʰ

lanet (naked eye) visibility
vening: Mercury (4th to 24th), Venus, Mars
ll night: Jupiter
Morning: Saturn

January 2015

The Sun is in Sagittarius but on Jan 19 moves into Capricorn which could herald a cold period. That is enhanced by Venus (from Jan 2 to 24) and Mercury (from Jan 4) also in Capricorn. From Jan 21 Mercury is retrograde which reinforces the effect.

However Jupiter (until Jan 29) in Leo, and Pluto in Sagittarius mediate some warmth. Saturn and Uranus in Scorpio and Pisces may bring precipitation. Mars (from Jan 8) and Neptune provide Light influences from Aquarius where Venus joins them on Jan 24.

Northern Transplanting Time
Jan 3 20ʰ to Jan 18 5ʰ and
Jan 31 7ʰ to Feb 14
Southern Transplanting Time
Dec 21 to Jan 3 16ʰ and
Jan 18 10ʰ to Jan 30 23ʰ

The transplanting time is a good time for **pruning fruit trees, vines and hedges.** Fruit and Flower times are preferred for this work. Avoid unfavourable times (- - -).

Southern hemisphere harvest time for seeds
Fruit seeds: Jan 8 0ʰ to Jan 10 22ʰ and other Fruit times.
Flower seeds: Flower times.
Leaf seeds: Leaf times.
Root seeds: Root times.

When **milk processing** it is best to avoid unfavourable times (- - -). This applies to both butter and cheese making. Milk which has been produced at Warmth/Fruit times yields the highest butterfat content. This is also the case on days with a tendency for thunderstorms. Times of moon perigee (**Pg**) are almost always unfavourable for milk processing and even yoghurt will not turn out well. Starter cultures from such days decay rapidly and it is advisable to produce double the amount the day before. Milk loves Light and Warmth times best of all. Water times are unsuitable.

19

February 2015

All times in G...

Date	Const. of Moon	Solar & lunar aspects	Moon Trines	El'ment	Parts of the plant enhanced by Moon or planets	Weather

(Time scale: 0 1 2 3 4 5 6 7 8 9 10 11 12 13 14 15 16 17 18 19 20 21 22 23 24)

Northern Transplanting Time

Date	Const.	Aspects		El'ment	Plant parts	Weather
1 Sun	♊	☉-☷		L	Flower	
2 Mon	♋	13ʰ		L/W	Flower to 12ʰ · Leaf from 13ʰ	♄ St E
3 Tue	♋	○ 23ʰ		W	Leaf	
4 Wed	♌	7ʰ		W/H	Leaf to 6ʰ · Fruit from 7ʰ	St T
5 Thu	♌			H	Fruit	S
6 Fri	♌	**Ag** 6ʰ		H	Fruit	
7 Sat	♍	6ʰ		H/E	Fruit to 5ʰ · Root from 6ʰ	♄ E
8 Sun	♍	♌ 17ʰ		E	Root to 13ʰ · · · · Rt 20ʰ	
9 Mon	♍			E	Root	♄StEqVoT
10 Tue	♍			E	Root	
11 Wed	♎	2ʰ		E/L	1ʰ · Flower from 2ʰ	S
12 Thu	♏	13ʰ ☽ 4ʰ		L/W	Flower to 12ʰ · Leaf from 13ʰ	
13 Fri	♏			W	Leaf	
14 Sat	♐	20ʰ ♆ 17ʰ		W/H	Leaf to 19ʰ · Fruit 20ʰ	♄ Vo T

Southern Transplanting Time

Date	Const.	Aspects		El'ment	Plant parts	Weather
15 Sun	♐	☉-♒		H	Fruit	Vo T
16 Mon	♑	22ʰ		H/E	Fruit to 21ʰ · 22ʰ	
17 Tue	♑			E	Root	♄ St E
18 Wed	♒	19ʰ ● 24ʰ		E/L	Root to 18ʰ · · · ·	St Vo T
19 Thu	♒	**Pg** 7ʰ		L	· · · · Fl 20ʰ	
20 Fri	♓	10ʰ		L/W	Flower to 9ʰ · Leaf from 10ʰ	
21 Sat	♓	☍ 16ʰ ·♂☉		W	Leaf to 12ʰ · · · · 19-21 · · ·	S
22 Sun	♓			W	Leaf from 1ʰ to 23ʰ	
23 Mon	♈	0ʰ		H	Fruit from 0ʰ to 12ʰ · · · ·	S
24 Tue	♉	18ʰ	☿☍ ▲	H/E	· · · ·	
25 Wed	♉	☽ 17ʰ		E	Root from 0ʰ to 14ʰ · Leaf from 15ʰ	
26 Thu	♉		▲	E	Leaf to 5ʰ · Root from 6ʰ	
27 Fri	♊	13ʰ ⌢ 7ʰ		E/L	Root to 12ʰ · Flower from 13ʰ	St Eq
28 Sat	♊			L	Flower	

(0 1 2 3 4 5 6 7 8 9 10 11 12 13 14 15 16 17 18 19 20 21 22 23 24)

Mercury ☿	Venus ♀	Mars ♂	Jupiter ♃	Saturn ♄	Uranus ♅	Neptune ♆	Pluto ♇
♑	♒	♒	♋	♏	♓	♒	♐
(R, 11 D)	14 ♓	9 ♓	(R)				

NB: All zodiac symbols refer to astronomical constellations, not astrological signs (see p. 1...

anetary aspects
(Bold = *visible to naked eye*)

☽☍♇ 11^{h} ♀☌♆ 18^{h}

☽☍☿ 6^{h}
☾☌♃ 6^{h}
☾☍♆ 19^{h}
☾☍♀ 6^{h} ⊙☍♃ 18^{h} ☾☍♂ 22^{h}

☾☍⛢ 22^{h}

☾☌♄ 1^{h}

☾☌♇ 23^{h}

☾☌☿ 5^{h}
☾☍♃ 2^{h}
☽☌♆ 11^{h}

☽☌♀ 0^{h} ☽☌♂ 0^{h} ☽●⛢ 22^{h}

♀☌♂ 5^{h}

☿☋ 13^{h} ♀△♄ 15^{h}
☽☍♄ 13^{h}
♂△♄ 3^{h} ⊙☌♆ 5^{h}

☽☍♇ 18^{h}

anet (naked eye) visibility
vening: Venus, Mars
ll night: Jupiter
orning: Saturn, Mercury (from 14th, Southern Hem. only)

February 2015

The Sun moves from Capricorn to Aquarius on Feb 15, bringing Light influences together with Neptune. Venus and Mars begin in the same Light constellation of Aquarius and move to watery Pisces on Feb 14 and 9. Together with Jupiter moving retrograde in Cancer, Saturn in Scorpio and Uranus in Pisces there are strong Water influences to bring precipitation.

Only Mercury (moving retrograde to Feb 11) in Capricorn brings cold, while Pluto in Sagittarius mediates warmth.

Northern Transplanting Time
Jan 31 to Feb 14 16^{h} and
Feb 27 13^{h} to March 14
Southern Transplanting Time
Feb 14 20^{h} to Feb 27 6^{h}

Vines, fruit trees and shrubs can be pruned during the transplanting period selecting Flower and Fruit times in preference. Unfavourable times (- - -) should be avoided.

Southern hemisphere harvest time for seeds
Fruit seeds: Any Fruit times during this month.
Flower seeds: Flower times from Feb 20.

Control slugs from Feb 2 13^{h} to Feb 4 6^{h}.

Best times for taking **willow cuttings for hedges and fences:** Jan 31 7^{h} to Feb 2 12^{h}, from Feb 4 7^{h} to Feb 7 5^{h}.

March 2015

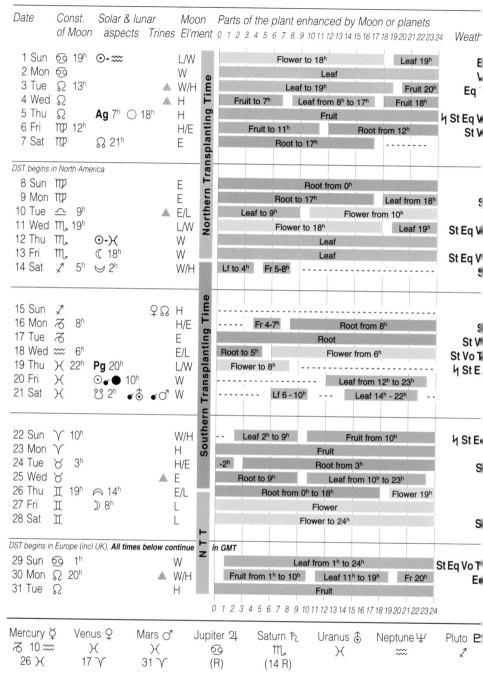

Date	Const. of Moon	Solar & lunar aspects	Moon Trines	El'ment	Parts of the plant enhanced by Moon or planets 0 1 2 3 4 5 6 7 8 9 10 11 12 13 14 15 16 17 18 19 20 21 22 23 24	Weath
1 Sun	♋ 19ʰ	☉-♒		L/W	Flower to 18ʰ / Leaf 19ʰ	E
2 Mon	♋			W	Leaf	W
3 Tue	♌ 13ʰ		▲	W/H	Leaf to 19ʰ / Fruit 20ʰ	Eq
4 Wed	♌		▲	H	Fruit to 7ʰ / Leaf from 8ʰ to 17ʰ / Fruit 18ʰ	
5 Thu	♌	Ag 7ʰ ○ 18ʰ		H	Fruit	♄ St Eq
6 Fri	♍ 12ʰ			H/E	Fruit to 11ʰ / Root from 12ʰ	St W
7 Sat	♍	♋ 21ʰ		E	Root to 17ʰ	

DST begins in North America

8 Sun	♍			E	Root from 0ʰ	
9 Mon	♍			E	Root to 17ʰ / Leaf from 18ʰ	S
10 Tue	♎ 9ʰ		▲	E/L	Leaf to 9ʰ / Flower from 10ʰ	
11 Wed	♏ 19ʰ			L/W	Flower to 18ʰ / Leaf 19ʰ	St Eq W
12 Thu	♏	☉-♓		W	Leaf	St Eq W
13 Fri	♏	☽ 18ʰ		W	Leaf	St Eq W
14 Sat	♐ 5ʰ	☙ 2ʰ		W/H	Lf to 4ʰ Fr 5-8ʰ	S

15 Sun	♐		♀♌	H		
16 Mon	♑ 8ʰ			H/E	Fr 4-7ʰ / Root from 8ʰ	
17 Tue	♑			E	Root	St W
18 Wed	♒ 6ʰ			E/L	Root to 5ʰ / Flower from 6ʰ	St Vo T
19 Thu	♓ 22ʰ	Pg 20ʰ		L/W	Flower to 8ʰ	♄ St E
20 Fri	♓	☉●● 10ʰ		W	Leaf from 12ʰ to 23ʰ	
21 Sat	♓	☍ 2ʰ ●♁ ●♂		W	Lf 6 - 10ʰ / Leaf 14ʰ - 22ʰ	

22 Sun	♈ 10ʰ			W/H	Leaf 2ʰ to 9ʰ / Fruit from 10ʰ	♄ St E
23 Mon	♈			H	Fruit	
24 Tue	♉ 3ʰ			H/E	-2ʰ / Root from 3ʰ	S
25 Wed	♉		▲	E	Root to 9ʰ / Leaf from 10ʰ to 23ʰ	
26 Thu	♊ 19ʰ	⌒ 14ʰ		E/L	Root from 0ʰ to 18ʰ / Flower 19ʰ	
27 Fri	♊	☽ 8ʰ		L	Flower	
28 Sat	♊			L	Flower to 24ʰ	S

*DST begins in Europe (incl UK). **All times below continue** in GMT*

29 Sun	♋ 1ʰ			W	Leaf from 1ʰ to 24ʰ	St Eq Vo T
30 Mon	♌ 20ʰ		▲	W/H	Fruit from 1ʰ to 10ʰ / Leaf 11ʰ to 19ʰ / Fr 20ʰ	E●
31 Tue	♌			H	Fruit	

0 1 2 3 4 5 6 7 8 9 10 11 12 13 14 15 16 17 18 19 20 21 22 23 24

Northern Transplanting Time — Southern Transplanting Time — N T T

Mercury ☿	Venus ♀	Mars ♂	Jupiter ♃	Saturn ♄	Uranus ⚸	Neptune ♆	Pluto ♇
♑ 10 ♒	♓	♓	♋	♏	♓	♒	♐
26 ♓	17 ♈	31 ♈	(R)	(14 R)			

NB: All zodiac symbols refer to astronomical constellations, not astrological signs (see p.1

netary aspects
(Bold = *visible to naked eye*)

☿☍♃ 21ʰ

☽☌♃ 5ʰ ☽☍☿ 9ʰ ♃△☌ 13ʰ
♀△♃ 15ʰ ♀☌☌ 19ʰ
☽☍♆ 3ʰ

☾☍♂ 2ʰ ☾☍☌ 7ʰ ☾☍♀ 16ʰ

♂△♃ 6ʰ
♂☌☌ 16ʰ
☾☌♄ 9ʰ

☾☌♇ 9ʰ ♀☊ 17ʰ

☾☍♃ 8ʰ
☿☌♆ 9ʰ
☾☌♆ 0ʰ ☾☌☿ 1ʰ

☽☌☌ 11ʰ ☽☌♂ 23ʰ

☽☌♀ 22ʰ

☽☍♄ 22ʰ
☉△♄ 19ʰ

☽☍♇ 1ʰ

☽☌♃ 7ʰ ♀△♇ 8ʰ

net (naked eye) visibility
ening: Venus, Mars
night: Jupiter
orning: Saturn, Mercury (to 6th, Southern Hem. only)

March 2015

On March 12 the Sun moves from Aquarius into Pisces. Together with Venus (to March 17), Mars and Uranus in Pisces, and Jupiter and Saturn retrograde in Cancer and Scorpio, most of the planets are conspiring to bring precipitation. This is reinforced by four Water trines in March. Only Pluto and (after March 17) Venus may mediate warmth, while Neptune and Mercury (from Jan 10 to 26) in Aquarius bring Light influences.

Northern Transplanting Time
Feb 27 to March 14 1ʰ and
March 26 19ʰ to April 10
Southern Transplanting Time
March 14 5ʰ to March 26 13ʰ

Southern hemisphere harvest time for seeds
Fruit seeds: at Fruit times, especially when Moon is in Leo (March 3 20ʰ to March 6 11ʰ) avoiding brief Leaf time on March 4.
Flower seeds: at Flower times.
Leaf seeds: Leaf times.
Root seeds: Root times, especially when Moon is in Capricorn (March 16 8ʰ to March 18 5ʰ).

Willow cuttings for **pollen production** are best cut from March 26 19ʰ to March 28 24ʰ; and for **honey flow** from March 3 20ʰ to March 6 11ʰ, avoiding brief Leaf time on March 4; and March 30 20ʰ to April 2 1ʰ.
    The cuttings taken in February are best stuck in the ground during transplanting time; to improve pollen production do this at Flower times, and to increase honey flow do this at Fruit times.

Control slugs from March 1 19ʰ to March 3 19ʰ.

Cuttings for grafting: March 14 5ʰ to March 26 14ʰ – that is, during ascending Moon – always choosing times (Fruit, Leaf, etc.) according to part of plant to be enhanced.

April 2015

All times in C

Date	Const. of Moon	Solar & lunar aspects	Trines	Moon El'ment	Parts of the plant enhanced by Moon or planets	Weath

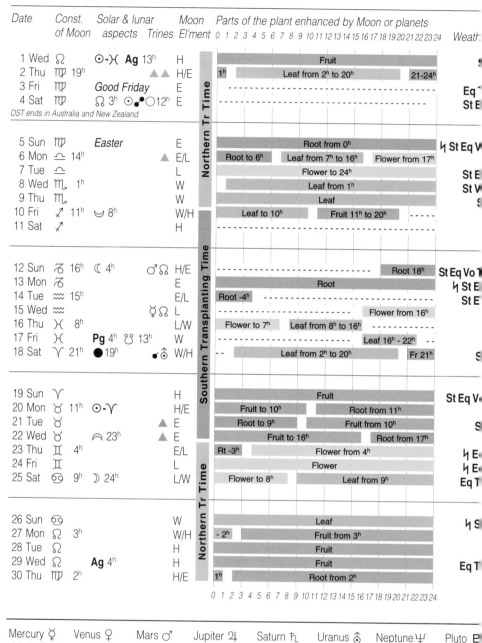

1 Wed	♌	☉-)(**Ag** 13ʰ		H	Fruit	
2 Thu	♍ 19ʰ		▲▲	H/E	1ʰ Leaf from 2ʰ to 20ʰ 21-24ʰ	
3 Fri	♍	*Good Friday*		E	Eq
4 Sat	♍	♌ 3ʰ ☉●○12ʰ		E	St E

DST ends in Australia and New Zealand

5 Sun	♍	*Easter*		E	Root from 0ʰ	♄ St Eq V
6 Mon	♎ 14ʰ		▲	E/L	Root to 6ʰ Leaf from 7ʰ to 16ʰ Flower from 17ʰ	
7 Tue	♎			L	Flower to 24ʰ	St E
8 Wed	♏ 1ʰ			W	Leaf from 1ʰ	St V
9 Thu	♏			W	Leaf	
10 Fri	♐ 11ʰ	☾ 8ʰ		W/H	Leaf to 10ʰ Fruit 11ʰ to 20ʰ	
11 Sat	♐			H		

12 Sun	♑ 16ʰ	☾ 4ʰ	♂♌	H/E	Root 18ʰ	St Eq Vo
13 Mon	♑			E	Root	♄ St E
14 Tue	♒ 15ʰ			E/L	Root -4ʰ	St E
15 Wed	♒		☿♌	L	Flower from 16ʰ	
16 Thu	)(8ʰ			L/W	Flower to 7ʰ Leaf from 8ʰ to 16ʰ	
17 Fri	)(	**Pg** 4ʰ ☍ 13ʰ		W	Leaf 16ʰ - 22ʰ	
18 Sat	♈ 21ʰ	●19ʰ	●♁	W/H	Leaf from 2ʰ to 20ʰ Fr 21ʰ	

19 Sun	♈			H	Fruit	St Eq V
20 Mon	♉ 11ʰ	☉-♈		H/E	Fruit to 10ʰ Root from 11ʰ	
21 Tue	♉		▲	E	Root to 9ʰ Fruit from 10ʰ	S
22 Wed	♉	☌ 23ʰ	▲	E	Fruit to 16ʰ Root from 17ʰ	
23 Thu	♊ 4ʰ			E/L	Rt -3ʰ Flower from 4ʰ	♄ E
24 Fri	♊			L	Flower	♄ E
25 Sat	♋ 9ʰ	☽ 24ʰ		L/W	Flower to 8ʰ Leaf from 9ʰ	Eq T

26 Sun	♋			W	Leaf	♄ S
27 Mon	♌ 3ʰ			W/H	- 2ʰ Fruit from 3ʰ	
28 Tue	♌			H	Fruit	
29 Wed	♌	**Ag** 4ʰ		H	Fruit	Eq T
30 Thu	♍ 2ʰ			H/E	1ʰ Root from 2ʰ	

0 1 2 3 4 5 6 7 8 9 10 11 12 13 14 15 16 17 18 19 20 21 22 23 24

Mercury ☿	Venus ♀	Mars ♂	Jupiter ♃	Saturn ♄	Uranus ♁	Neptune ♆	Pluto ♇
)(14 ♈	♈	♈	♋	♏	)(	♒	♐
27 ♉	6 ♉		(R, 8 D)	(R)			(17 R)

NB: All zodiac symbols refer to astronomical constellations, not astrological signs (see p.

Planetary aspects
(Bold = *visible to naked eye*)

1 ☽☌♅ 12^h
2 ☿△♄ 12^h ☉△♃ 17^h
3 ☽☍☿ 22^h
4 ☾☍⊕ 16^h

5
6 ☾☍♂ 3^h ☉☌⊕ 14^h ☿△♃ 14^h
7 ☾☍♀ 21^h
8 ☿☌⊕ 12^h **☾☌♄ 14^h**
9
10 ☉☌☿ 4^h
11 ☾☌♇ 17^h

12 ♂☊ 7^h
13 ☾☌♃ 15^h
14
15 ♀☌♄ 4^h ☿☊ 5^h ☾☌♅ 11^h
16
17
18 ☾●⊕ 1^h

19 ☽☌☿ 13^h ☽☌♂ 21^h
20
21 ☽☍♄ 6^h **☽☌♀ 20^h** ♂△♇ 22^h
22 ☿△♇ 13^h
23 ☿☌♂ 0^h
24 ☽☍♇ 9^h
25

26 **☽☌♃ 15^h**
27
28 ☽☍♅ 20^h
29
30

Planet (naked eye) visibility
Evening: Venus, Mars (to 16th), Jupiter
All night: Saturn
Morning:

April 2015

Pisces harbours the Sun until April 20, Mercury until April 14 and Uranus all month. Together with Jupiter in Cancer and Saturn retrograde in Scorpio, this could well bring rain. In the first few days of the month there are three Water trines.

In the second part of the month, the Sun (from April 20) and Mercury (from April 14 to 27) join Mars in Aries, and the Warmth influence is supported by Pluto (retrograde from April 17) in Sagittarius. This is reinforced by Warmth trines on April 21 and 22. A cold influences comes from Venus (from April 6) and Mercury (in the last four days of the month) in Taurus. Only Neptune in Aquarius may bring Light influences.

The rain of the first half of the month may change to warm and sunny spring days.

Northern Transplanting Time
March 26 to April 10 7^h and
April 23 4^h to May 7
Southern Transplanting Time
April 10 11^h to April 22 22^h

Grafting of fruiting shrubs from April 10 11^h to April 11 7^h and April 18 21^h to April 20 10^h.
Grafting of flowering shrubs from April 15 16^h to April 16 7^h.

Control slugs from April 25 9^h to April 27 2^h.

Southern hemisphere harvest time for seeds
Choose Fruit, Flower, Leaf, Root times according to type of plant, and avoid unfavourable times (- - -). For Fruit, particularly when Moon is in Leo, and for Root, Moon in Capricorn is preferable.

Biodynamic preparations: Birch should be cut, filled with yarrow and hung up on April 22 between 2^h and 17^h.

25

May 2015

All times in GM

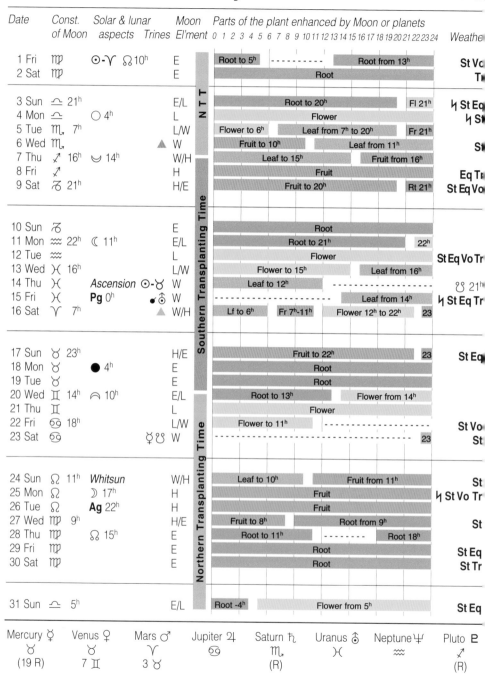

Date	Const. of Moon	Solar & lunar aspects	Trines	Moon El'ment	Transplanting	Parts of the plant enhanced by Moon or planets (0–24h)	Weathe
1 Fri	♍	⊙-♈ ☊10h		E	N T T	Root to 5h - - - - Root from 13h	St Vo
2 Sat	♍			E	N T T	Root	T
3 Sun	♎ 21h			E/L	N T T	Root to 20h; Fl 21h	♄ St Eq
4 Mon	♎	○ 4h		L	N T T	Flower	♄ St
5 Tue	♏ 7h			L/W	N T T	Flower to 6h; Leaf from 7h to 20h; Fr 21h	
6 Wed	♏		▲	W	N T T	Fruit to 10h; Leaf from 11h	St
7 Thu	♐ 16h	◡ 14h		W/H	Southern Transplanting Time	Leaf to 15h; Fruit from 16h	
8 Fri	♐			H	Southern Transplanting Time	Fruit	Eq Tr
9 Sat	♑ 21h			H/E	Southern Transplanting Time	Fruit to 20h; Rt 21h	St Eq Vo
10 Sun	♑			E	Southern Transplanting Time	Root	
11 Mon	♒ 22h	☾ 11h		E/L	Southern Transplanting Time	Root to 21h; 22h	
12 Tue	♒			L	Southern Transplanting Time	Flower	St Eq Vo Tr
13 Wed	♓ 16h			L/W	Southern Transplanting Time	Flower to 15h; Leaf from 16h	
14 Thu	♓	*Ascension* ⊙-♉		W	Southern Transplanting Time	Leaf to 12h - - - -	☋ 21h
15 Fri	♓	**Pg** 0h	☌♅	W	Southern Transplanting Time	- - - - Leaf from 14h	♄ St Eq Tr
16 Sat	♈ 7h		▲	W/H	Southern Transplanting Time	Lf to 6h; Fr 7h-11h; Flower 12h to 22h; 23	
17 Sun	♉ 23h			H/E	Southern Transplanting Time	Fruit to 22h; 23	St Eq
18 Mon	♉	● 4h		E	Southern Transplanting Time	Root	
19 Tue	♉			E	Southern Transplanting Time	Root	
20 Wed	♊ 14h	⌢ 10h		E/L	Northern Transplanting Time	Root to 13h; Flower from 14h	
21 Thu	♊			L	Northern Transplanting Time	Flower	
22 Fri	♋ 18h			L/W	Northern Transplanting Time	Flower to 11h - - - -	St Vo
23 Sat	♋		☿☋	W	Northern Transplanting Time	- - - - 23	St
24 Sun	♌ 11h	*Whitsun*		W/H	Northern Transplanting Time	Leaf to 10h; Fruit from 11h	St
25 Mon	♌	☽ 17h		H	Northern Transplanting Time	Fruit	♄ St Vo Tr
26 Tue	♌	**Ag** 22h		H	Northern Transplanting Time	Fruit	
27 Wed	♍ 9h			H/E	Northern Transplanting Time	Fruit to 8h; Root from 9h	St
28 Thu	♍	☋ 15h		E	Northern Transplanting Time	Root to 11h - - - - Root 18h	
29 Fri	♍			E	Northern Transplanting Time	Root	St Eq
30 Sat	♍			E	Northern Transplanting Time	Root	St Tr
31 Sun	♎ 5h			E/L	Northern Transplanting Time	Root -4h; Flower from 5h	St Eq

Mercury ☿	Venus ♀	Mars ♂	Jupiter ♃	Saturn ♄	Uranus ♅	Neptune ♆	Pluto ♇
♉	♉	♈	♋	♏	♓	♒	♐
(19 R)	7 ♊	3 ♉		(R)			(R)

NB: All zodiac symbols refer to astronomical constellations, not astrological signs (see p. 10

lanetary aspects
(Bold = *visible to naked eye*)

1
2 ☽☍♃ 2ʰ

3 ☿☍♄ 9ʰ
4
5 ☾☌♂ 2ʰ ☾☌♄ 17ʰ ☾☍☿ 23ʰ
6 ☉△♇ 7ʰ
7 ☾☍♀ 18ʰ
8 ☾☌♇ 22ʰ
9

0
1 ☾☍♃ 0ʰ
2 ☾☌♆ 19ʰ
3
4
5 ♂☍♄ 6ʰ ☾●♃ 12ʰ
6 ♀△♆ 19ʰ

7
8 ☽☍♄ 13ʰ ☽☌♂ 17ʰ
9 ☽☌☿ 8ʰ
0
1 ☽☌♀ 17ʰ ☽☍♇ 18ʰ
2 ♀☍♇ 2ʰ
3 ☉☍♄ 1ʰ ☿☊ 12ʰ

4 ☽☌♃ 4ʰ
5
6 ☽☍♆ 5ʰ
7 ☿☌♂ 11ʰ
8
9 ☽☍♃ 12ʰ
0 ☉☌☿ 17ʰ

1

lanet (naked eye) visibility
vening: Venus, Jupiter, Mercury (1st to 15th)
ll night: Saturn
Morning:

May 2015

The Sun moves from Aries to cooler Taurus on May 14. Mercury, retrograde, and Mars (from May 3) in Taurus also bring their cool influence. Saturn, retrograde in Sorpio, is supported by Jupiter (in Cancer) and Uranus (in Pisces) in bringing rain.

Neptune in Aquarius and, from May 7, Venus in Gemini bring Light influences, including a Light trine on May 16. After Mars moves out of Aries on May 3, only Pluto, retrograde in Sagittarius, brings Warmth influences.

Northern Transplanting Time
April 23 to May 7 12ʰ and
May 20 14ʰ to June 3
Southern Transplanting Time
May 7 16ʰ to May 20 8ʰ

The **soil warms up** on May 6.

Plant **table potatoes** at Root times, in late districts best time is May 27 9ʰ to May 31 4ʰ, avoiding unfavourable times (- - -). **Transplant seed potatoes** for 2016 from May 16 7ʰ to 11ʰ and May 16 23ʰ to May 17 22ʰ.

Hay should be cut at Flower times after May 7.

Control:
Insect pests, Colorado beetle and varroa from May 17 23ʰ to May 20 13ʰ.
Flies by burning fly papers in the cow barn at Flower times after May 7.
Mole crickets from May 5 7ʰ to 20ʰ and May 6 11ʰ to May 7 15ʰ.

Begin **queen bee** rearing at Flower times, especially when Moon is in Gemini (May 20 14ʰ to May 22 11ʰ).

Biodynamic preparations should be dug out from May 5 22ʰ to May 6 11ʰ.

27

June 2015

| Date | Const. of Moon | Solar & lunar aspects | Moon Trines | El'ment | Parts of the plant enhanced by Moon or planets 0 1 2 3 4 5 6 7 8 9 10 11 12 13 14 15 16 17 18 19 20 21 22 23 24 | Weathe[...] |

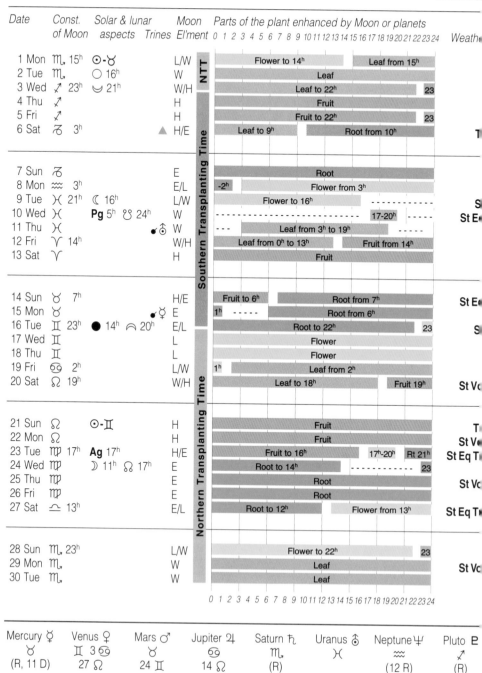

1 Mon	♏ 15ʰ	☉-♉		L/W
2 Tue	♏	○ 16ʰ		W
3 Wed	♐ 23ʰ	☋ 21ʰ		W/H
4 Thu	♐			H
5 Fri	♐			H
6 Sat	♑ 3ʰ		▲	H/E

NTT — Flower to 14ʰ / Leaf from 15ʰ
Leaf
Leaf to 22ʰ · 23
Fruit
Fruit to 22ʰ · 23
Leaf to 9ʰ / Root from 10ʰ — T[...]

Southern Transplanting Time

7 Sun	♑			E
8 Mon	♒ 3ʰ			E/L
9 Tue	♓ 21ʰ	☾ 16ʰ		L/W
10 Wed	♓	Pg 5ʰ ☍ 24ʰ		W
11 Thu	♓		⚹ ♅	W
12 Fri	♈ 14ʰ			W/H
13 Sat	♈			H

Root
-2ʰ Flower from 3ʰ
Flower to 16ʰ
17-20ʰ
Leaf from 3ʰ to 19ʰ
Leaf from 0ʰ to 13ʰ / Fruit from 14ʰ
Fruit

14 Sun	♉ 7ʰ			H/E
15 Mon	♉		⚹ ☿	E
16 Tue	♊ 23ʰ	● 14ʰ ⚼ 20ʰ		E/L
17 Wed	♊			L
18 Thu	♊			L
19 Fri	♋ 2ʰ			L/W
20 Sat	♌ 19ʰ			W/H

Fruit to 6ʰ / Root from 7ʰ — St E[...]
1ʰ Root from 6ʰ
Root to 22ʰ · 23 — S[...]
Flower
Flower
1ʰ Leaf from 2ʰ
Leaf to 18ʰ / Fruit 19ʰ — St V[...]

Northern Transplanting Time

21 Sun	♌	☉-♊		H
22 Mon	♌			H
23 Tue	♍ 17ʰ	Ag 17ʰ		H/E
24 Wed	♍	☽ 11ʰ ♌ 17ʰ		E
25 Thu	♍			E
26 Fri	♍			E
27 Sat	♎ 13ʰ			E/L

Fruit — T[...]
Fruit — St V[...]
Fruit to 16ʰ / 17ʰ-20ʰ Rt 21ʰ — St Eq T[...]
Root to 14ʰ · 23
Root — St V[...]
Root
Root to 12ʰ / Flower from 13ʰ — St Eq T[...]

28 Sun	♏ 23ʰ			L/W
29 Mon	♏			W
30 Tue	♏			W

Flower to 22ʰ · 23
Leaf — St V[...]
Leaf

0 1 2 3 4 5 6 7 8 9 10 11 12 13 14 15 16 17 18 19 20 21 22 23 24

Mercury ☿	Venus ♀	Mars ♂	Jupiter ♃	Saturn ♄	Uranus ♅	Neptune ♆	Pluto ♇
♉	♊ 3 ♋	♉	♋	♏	♓	♒	♐
(R, 11 D)	27 ♌	24 ♊	14 ♌	(R)	(12 R)		(R)

NB: All zodiac symbols refer to astronomical constellations, not astrological signs (see p. 1[...])

Planetary aspects
(Bold = visible to naked eye)

1	**☽ ☌ ♄ 20ʰ**
2	☽ ☍ ☿ 8ʰ ☾ ☍ ♂ 23ʰ
3	
4	
5	☾ ☌ ♇ 3ʰ
6	♀ △ ♄ 6ʰ ☾ ☍ ♀ 6ʰ
7	☾ ☍ ♃ 11ʰ
8	
9	☾ ☌ ♆ 1ʰ
10	
11	☾ • ⊕ 21ʰ
12	
13	
14	☉ ☌ ♂ 15ʰ ☾ ☌ ♄ 18ʰ
15	☾ • ☿ 2ʰ
16	☾ ☌ ♂ 13ʰ
17	
18	☽ ☍ ♇ 2ʰ
19	
20	☽ ☌ ♀ 8ʰ ☽ ☌ ♃ 21ʰ
21	
22	☽ ☍ ♆ 13ʰ ♃ △ ⊕ 14ʰ
23	
24	
25	☽ ☍ ⊕ 22ʰ
26	
27	
28	
29	☽ ☌ ♄ 2ʰ ♀ △ ⊕ 6ʰ
30	☽ ☍ ☿ 10ʰ

The Sun moves from Taurus to Gemini on June 21 and is joined by Mars three days later. Together with Neptune (retrograde from June 12) in Aquarius this will ensure Light influences. Taurus gives space to Mercury (moving retrograde from June 11) and Mars (until June 24). This may bring cool weather, at least at night.

Saturn in Scorpio is retrograde, thus making the Water influence particularly strong. This is supported by Venus (from June 3 to 27) and Jupiter (until June 14) in Cancer and Uranus in Pisces. There is a strong likelihood of rain. Pluto, retrograde, in the Warmth constellation of Sagittarius, is helped by Jupiter in Leo (from June 14) to bring warmth. The planets are balanced between the different elements, and it will be interesting to see which prevail.

Northern Transplanting Time
May 20 to June 3 20ʰ and
June 16 23ʰ to July 1
Southern Transplanting Time
June 3 23ʰ to June 16 18ʰ

Cut **hay** at Flower times.

Begin **queen bee** rearing at Flower times, particularly when Moon is in Gemini (June 16 23ʰ to June 19 1ʰ).

Control:
Flies by burning fly papers in the cow barn at Flower times.
Mole crickets ash from June 1 15ʰ to June 3 22ʰ.
Grasshoppers in July.

June

Planet (naked eye) visibility
Evening: Venus, Jupiter
All night: Saturn
Morning: Mercury (from 14th, Southern Hemisphere only)

July 2015

All times in G

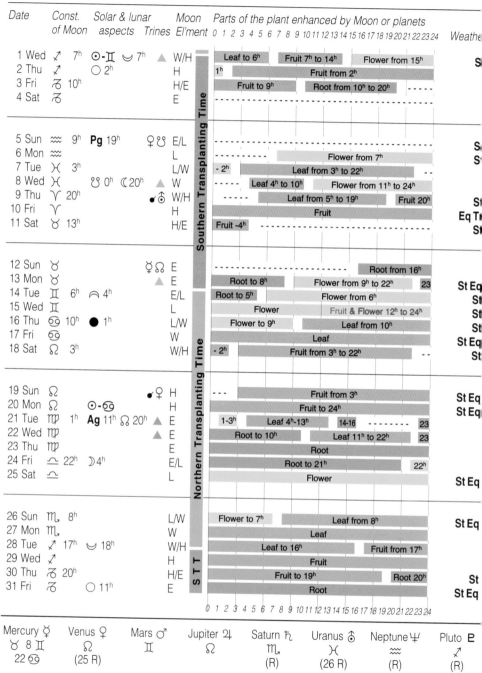

Date	Const. of Moon	Solar & lunar aspects	Moon Trines	El'ment	Parts of the plant enhanced by Moon or planets	Weather

Mercury ☿ ♉ 8 ♊ 22 ♋
Venus ♀ ♌ (25 R)
Mars ♂ ♊
Jupiter ♃ ♌
Saturn ♄ ♏ (R)
Uranus ♅ ♈ (26 R)
Neptune ♆ ♒ (R)
Pluto ♇ ♐ (R)

30

NB: All zodiac symbols refer to astronomical constellations, not astrological signs (see p.10)

Planetary aspects
(Bold = visible to naked eye)

1 ♀☌♃ 8ʰ ☽☍♂ 18ʰ ☉△♆ 21ʰ
2 ☽☌♇ 10ʰ
3
4

5 ☽☍♃ 2ʰ ☽☍♀ 5ʰ ♀☍ 6ʰ
6 ☽☌♅ 7ʰ ☉☍♇ 15ʰ
7
8 ♂△♆ 23ʰ
9 ☽●☍ 3ʰ
10
11 ☽☍♄ 22ʰ

12 ☿☍ 4ʰ
13 ☿△♆ 19ʰ
14
15 ☽☌☿ 5ʰ ☽☌♂ 8ʰ ☽☍♇ 8ʰ ♂☍♇ 14ʰ
16 ☿☍♇ 0ʰ ☿☌♂ 4ʰ
17
18 ☽☌♃ 15ʰ

19 ☽●♀ 1ʰ ☽☍♆ 20ʰ
20
21 ☉△♄ 11ʰ
22 ☿△♄ 18ʰ
23 ☽☍☉ 7ʰ ☉☌☿ 20ʰ
24
25

26 ☽☌♄ 9ʰ
27
28
29 ☽☌♇ 18ʰ
30 ☽☍♂ 11ʰ
31

Planet (naked eye) visibility
Evening: Venus, Jupiter (to 31st)
All night: Saturn
Morning: Mercury (to 4th, Southern Hemisphere only)

July 2015

The Sun moving from Gemini into Cancer on July 20 could bring some warm rain showers.

Mercury (from July 8 to 22) and Mars in Gemini bring Light influences which Neptune reinforces while retrograde in Aquarius. The Light character of the first half of July is further emphasised by three Light trines on July 1, 8 and 13. Against this, Saturn in Scorpio is retrograde, together with Uranus in Pisces (also retrograde from July 26) enhanced by two Water trines in July 21 and 22, this may make the second part of July wetter.

Jupiter and Venus in Leo support Pluto, retrograde in Sagittarius, in mediating Warmth.

Northern Transplanting Time
June 16 to July 1 6ʰ and
July 14 6ʰ to July 28 16ʰ
Southern Transplanting Time
July 1 8ʰ to July 14 3ʰ and
July 28 19ʰ to Aug 10

Late hay cut at Flower times, best when Moon is in Gemini (July 14 6ʰ to July 16 9ʰ).

Summer harvest for seeds:
Flower plants: Harvest at Flower times up to July 16.

Similarly, harvest **leaf plants** at Leaf times, and **root plants** at Root times (best July 3 10ʰ to 20ʰ). **Fruit plants** from July 18 3ʰ to July 20 24ʰ, avoiding unfavourable times (- - -).

Control
Grasshoppers: from July 14 6ʰ to July 16 9ʰ.
Flies: burn fly papers in the cow barn at Flower times, avoiding unfavourable times (- - -).
Slugs: spray leaf plants and the soil with horn silica early in the morning during Leaf times. Burn between July 16 10ʰ and July 18 2ʰ.

July

August 2015

All times in G

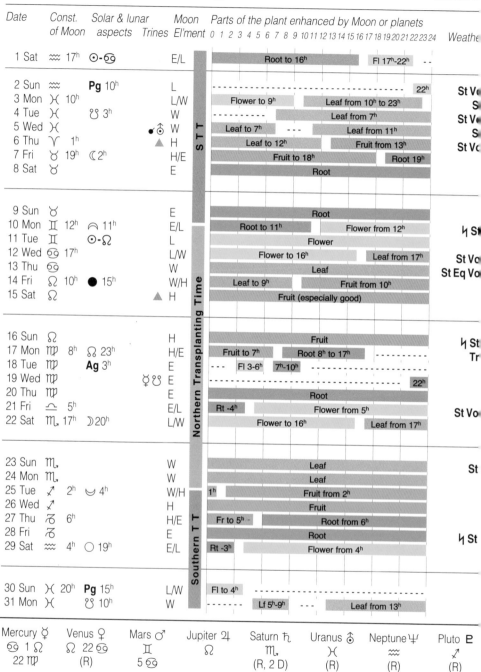

Date	Const. of Moon	Solar & lunar aspects	Moon Trines	Moon El'ment	Parts of the plant enhanced by Moon or planets	Weather
1 Sat	≈ 17h	☉-♋		E/L	Root to 16h — Fl 17h-22h	- -
2 Sun	≈	Pg 10h		L	22h	St V
3 Mon	♓ 10h			L/W	Flower to 9h — Leaf from 10h to 23h	S
4 Tue	♓	☊ 3h		W	Leaf from 7h	St V
5 Wed	♓		●♁	W	Leaf to 7h — Leaf from 11h	S
6 Thu	♈ 1h		▲	H	Leaf to 12h — Fruit from 13h	St V
7 Fri	♉ 19h	☾ 2h		H/E	Fruit to 18h — Root 19h	
8 Sat	♉			E	Root	
9 Sun	♉			E	Root	
10 Mon	♊ 12h	⚹ 11h		E/L	Root to 11h — Flower from 12h	♄ St
11 Tue	♊	☉-♌		L	Flower	
12 Wed	♋ 17h			L/W	Flower to 16h — Leaf from 17h	St V
13 Thu	♋			W	Leaf	St Eq V
14 Fri	♌ 10h	● 15h		W/H	Leaf to 9h — Fruit from 10h	
15 Sat	♌		▲	H	Fruit (especially good)	
16 Sun	♌			H	Fruit	♄ St
17 Mon	♍ 8h	♌ 23h		H/E	Fruit to 7h — Root 8h to 17h	Tr
18 Tue	♍	Ag 3h		E	Fl 3-6h — 7h-10h	
19 Wed	♍		☿♈	E	22h	
20 Thu	♍			E	Root	
21 Fri	♎ 5h			E/L	Rt -4h — Flower from 5h	St Vo
22 Sat	♏ 17h	☽ 20h		L/W	Flower to 16h — Leaf from 17h	
23 Sun	♏			W	Leaf	St
24 Mon	♏			W	Leaf	
25 Tue	♐ 2h	☋ 4h		W/H	1h — Fruit from 2h	
26 Wed	♐			H	Fruit	
27 Thu	♑ 6h			H/E	Fr to 5h — Root from 6h	
28 Fri	♑			E	Root	♄ St
29 Sat	≈ 4h	○ 19h		E/L	Rt -3h — Flower from 4h	
30 Sun	♓ 20h	Pg 15h		L/W	Fl to 4h	
31 Mon	♓	☊ 10h		W	Lf 5h-9h — Leaf from 13h	

STT — Northern Transplanting Time — Southern TT

Mercury ☿	Venus ♀	Mars ♂	Jupiter ♃	Saturn ♄	Uranus ♅	Neptune ♆	Pluto ♇
♋ 1 ♌	♌ 22 ♋	♊	♌	♏	♓	≈	♐
22 ♍	(R)	5 ♋		(R, 2 D)	(R)	(R)	(R)

NB: All zodiac symbols refer to astronomical constellations, not astrological signs (see p.10

Planetary aspects
(**Bold** = *visible to naked eye*)

1	☾☌☿ 2ʰ ☾☌♃ 19ʰ ☾☌♀ 22ʰ
2	☾☌♆ 13ʰ ☿△♁ 15ʰ
3	
4	♀☌♃ 22ʰ
5	☾•♁ 9ʰ
6	♂△♄ 9ʰ ☿☌♀ 14ʰ
7	☿☌♃ 7ʰ
8	☾☌♄ 3ʰ
9	
10	
11	☾☌♇ 13ʰ
12	
13	☿☍♆ 1ʰ ☾☌♂ 2ʰ ☉△♁ 10ʰ
14	☽☌♀ 18ʰ
15	☽☌♃ 9ʰ ☉☌♀ 19ʰ ☿△♇ 20ʰ
16	☽☍♆ 2ʰ ☽☌☿ 13ʰ
17	
18	
19	☿☍ 11ʰ ☽☍♁ 14ʰ ♀△♁ 17ʰ
20	
21	
22	☽☌♄ 18ʰ
23	
24	
25	
26	☽☌♇ 4ʰ ☉☌♃ 22ʰ
27	
28	☽☍♂ 4ʰ ☽☍♀ 10ʰ
29	☽☍♃ 15ʰ ☾☌♆ 22ʰ
30	
31	☾☍☿ 16ʰ

Planet (naked eye) visibility
Evening: Venus (to 5th), Saturn, Mercury (from 26th, SH)
All night:
Morning: Venus (from 25th), Mars (from 12th)

August 2015

The Sun moves into Leo on August 11, hopefully bringing warm summer weather. Pluto is still retrograde in Sagittarius, and supports the warmth. This is enhanced by Jupiter and, until Aug 22, Mercury and Venus in Leo. The latter then move in opposite directions: Mercury to Virgo and Venus retrograde to Cancer. There Venus joins Mars in ensuring precipitation. This is strengthened by Saturn in Scorpio, and Uranus retrograde in Pisces.

After Mars leaves Gemini on Aug 5, only Neptune, retrograde in Aquarius, will bring Light influences.

Northern Transplanting Time
Aug 10 12ʰ to Aug 25 3ʰ
Southern Transplanting Time
July 28 to Aug 10 10ʰ and Aug 25 5ʰ to Sep 6

Seeds of fruit plants and **grain** to be used for seed should be harvested at Fruit times, avoiding unfavourable times (- - -). Favourable times are Aug 14 10ʰ to Aug 17 7ʰ.

Immediately after harvest, sow catch crops like lupins, phacelia, mustard or wild flax.

Seeds for leaf plants: harvest at Leaf times, specially during Water trines (▲).

Seeds for flower plants: at Flower times.

Burn **fly papers** in the cow barn at Flower times.

Ants in the house: burn when the Moon is in Leo, Aug 14 10ʰ to Aug 17 7ʰ.

Biodynamic preparations: Cut larch and fill with chamomile and put it in the earth between Aug 12 16ʰ and Aug 13 9ʰ.

Aug

September 2015

All times in G

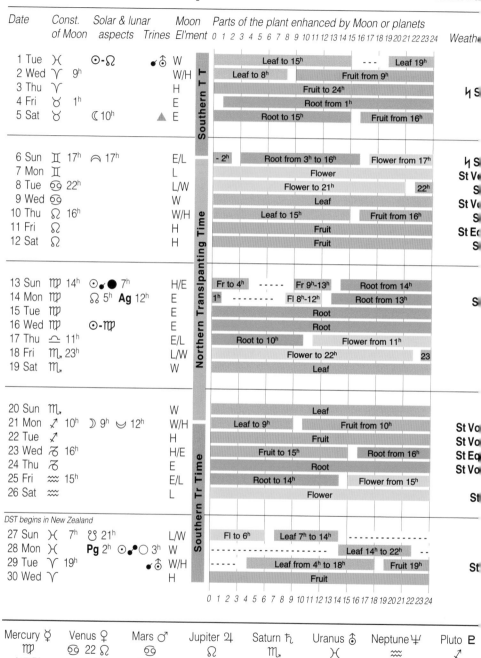

Date	Const. of Moon	Solar & lunar aspects	Moon Trines	El'ment	Parts of the plant enhanced by Moon or planets	Weath

Southern T T

Date	Const.	Solar & lunar aspects	Trines	El'ment	Plant parts	Weather
1 Tue	♓	☉-♌	☾☊ W	W	Leaf to 15ʰ · · · Leaf 19ʰ	
2 Wed	♈ 9ʰ			W/H	Leaf to 8ʰ Fruit from 9ʰ	
3 Thu	♈			H	Fruit to 24ʰ	♄ S
4 Fri	♉ 1ʰ			E	Root from 1ʰ	
5 Sat	♉	☾ 10ʰ	▲ E	E	Root to 15ʰ Fruit from 16ʰ	
6 Sun	♊ 17ʰ	♉ 17ʰ		E/L	- 2ʰ Root from 3ʰ to 16ʰ Flower from 17ʰ	♄ S
7 Mon	♊			L	Flower	St V
8 Tue	♋ 22ʰ			L/W	Flower to 21ʰ 22ʰ	S
9 Wed	♋			W	Leaf	St V
10 Thu	♌ 16ʰ			W/H	Leaf to 15ʰ Fruit from 16ʰ	S
11 Fri	♌			H	Fruit	St Ec
12 Sat	♌			H	Fruit	S
13 Sun	♍ 14ʰ	☉☽● 7ʰ		H/E	Fr to 4ʰ · · · · · Fr 9ʰ-13ʰ Root from 14ʰ	
14 Mon	♍	♌ 5ʰ **Ag** 12ʰ		E	1ʰ · · · · · · · Fl 8ʰ-12ʰ Root from 13ʰ	
15 Tue	♍			E	Root	S
16 Wed	♍	☉-♍		E	Root	
17 Thu	♎ 11ʰ			E/L	Root to 10ʰ Flower from 11ʰ	
18 Fri	♏ 23ʰ			L/W	Flower to 22ʰ 23	
19 Sat	♏			W	Leaf	
20 Sun	♏			W	Leaf	
21 Mon	♐ 10ʰ	☽ 9ʰ ☋ 12ʰ		W/H	Leaf to 9ʰ Fruit from 10ʰ	St V
22 Tue	♐			H	Fruit	St V
23 Wed	♑ 16ʰ			H/E	Fruit to 15ʰ Root from 16ʰ	St E
24 Thu	♑			E	Root	St V
25 Fri	♒ 15ʰ			E/L	Root to 14ʰ Flower from 15ʰ	St V
26 Sat	♒			L	Flower	St

DST begins in New Zealand

Date	Const.	Solar & lunar aspects	Trines	El'ment	Plant parts	Weather
27 Sun	♓ 7ʰ	☋ 21ʰ		L/W	Fl to 6ʰ Leaf 7ʰ to 14ʰ · · · · · · ·	
28 Mon	♓	**Pg** 2ʰ ☉☽○ 3ʰ		W	· · · · · · · Leaf 14ʰ to 22ʰ · ·	
29 Tue	♈ 19ʰ		☾☊	W/H	· · · · · Leaf from 4ʰ to 18ʰ Fruit 19ʰ	St
30 Wed	♈			H	Fruit	

0 1 2 3 4 5 6 7 8 9 10 11 12 13 14 15 16 17 18 19 20 21 22 23 24

Northern Transplanting Time / **Southern Tr Time**

Mercury ☿	Venus ♀	Mars ♂	Jupiter ♃	Saturn ♄	Uranus ♅	Neptune ♆	Pluto ♇
♍	♋ 22 ♌	♋	♌	♏	♓	♒	♐
(17 R)	(R, 6 D)	7 ♌			(R)	(R)	(R, 25 D)

NB: All zodiac symbols refer to astronomical constellations, not astrological signs (see p. 10

Planetary aspects
(**Bold** = *visible to naked eye*)

1   ☉♂♆ 4ʰ   ♀☌♂ 5ʰ   ☾●⊕ 17ʰ
2
3
4   ☾☌♄ 10ʰ
5   ☉△♇ 23ʰ

6
7   ☾☌♇ 18ʰ
8   ♂△⊕ 20ʰ
9
10   ☾☌♀ 7ʰ   ☾☌♂ 20ʰ
11
12   ☾☌♃ 4ʰ   ☾☌♆ 6ʰ

13
14
15   ☽☌☿ 11ʰ   ☽☌⊕ 18ʰ
16
17   ♃☌♆ 7ʰ
18
19   ☽☌♄ 4ʰ

20
21
22   ☽☌♇ 12ʰ
23   ♀△⊕ 4ʰ
24
25   ☽☌♀ 4ʰ   ☽☌♂ 21ʰ
26   ☽☌♆ 8ʰ   ☽☌♃ 12ʰ

27
28   ☾☌☿ 11ʰ
29   ☾●⊕ 2ʰ
30   ☉☌☿ 15ʰ

Planet (naked eye) visibility

Evening: Saturn, Mercury (to 14th, Southern Hem only)
All night:
Morning: Venus, Mars, Jupiter (from 8th)

September 2015

The Warmth trine on Sep 5, together with the Sun (until Sep 16), Mars (from Sep 7) and Jupiter in Leo, as well as Pluto in Sagittarius (retrograde until Sep 25) will bring warm days. Mercury, in Virgo all month and retrograde from Sep 17, is joined there by the Sun on Sep 16. This could bring cool, misty nights.

Venus in Cancer (until Sep 22), Saturn in Scorpio, and Uranus working strongly while retrograde in Pisces, will lead to precipitation. Only Neptune retrograde in Aquarius brings the influence of Light.

Northern Transplanting Time
Sep 6 18ʰ to Sep 21 11ʰ
Southern Transplanting Time
Aug 25 to Sep 6 16ʰ and Sep 21 13ʰ to Oct 3

The times recommended for the **fruit harvest** are those in which the Moon is in Aries or Sagittarius (Sep 2 9ʰ to Sep 3 24ʰ, and Sep 21 10ʰ to Sep 23 15ʰ, Sep 29 19ʰ to Oct 1 9ʰ) or other Fruit times.

The harvest of **root crops** is always best undertaken at Root times. Storage trials of onions, carrots, beetroot and potatoes have demonstrated this time and again.

Good times for **sowing winter grain** in later districts are from Sep 10 16ʰ to Sep 13 13ʰ avoiding the brief unfavourable time (- - -), and at other Fruit times.

Rye can if necessary also be sown at Root times with all subsequent cultivations being carried out at Fruit times.

Control ants in buildings by ashing them between Sep 10 16ʰ and Sep 13 13ʰ.
Slug control from Sep 8 22ʰ to Sep 10 15ʰ.

Biodynamic preparations: Cut maple (for dandelion) on Sep 14 from 1ʰ to 12ʰ.

Sep

October 2015

All times in GM

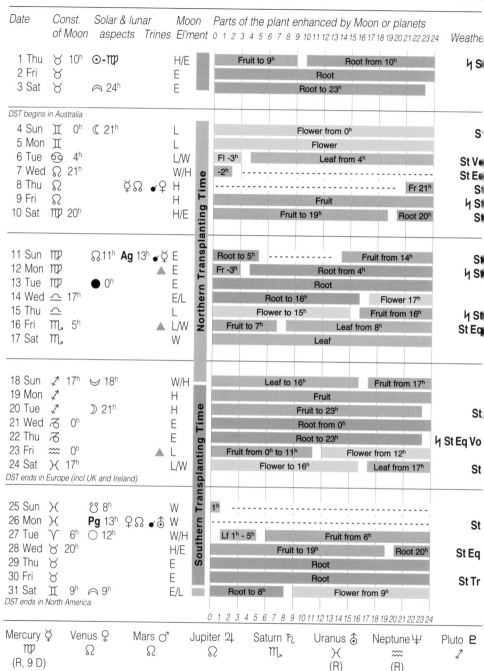

Date	Const. of Moon	Solar & lunar aspects	Moon Trines	El'ment	Parts of the plant enhanced by Moon or planets (0–24)	Weathe
1 Thu	♉ 10ʰ	☉-♍		H/E	Fruit to 9ʰ / Root from 10ʰ	♄ S
2 Fri	♉			E	Root	
3 Sat	♉	♑ 24ʰ		E	Root to 23ʰ	
DST begins in Australia						
4 Sun	♊ 0ʰ	☾ 21ʰ		L	Flower from 0ʰ	S
5 Mon	♊			L	Flower	
6 Tue	♋ 4ʰ			L/W	Fl -3ʰ / Leaf from 4ʰ	St V
7 Wed	♌ 21ʰ			W/H	-2ʰ	St E
8 Thu	♌	☿♌ ●♀		H	Fr 21ʰ	S
9 Fri	♌			H	Fruit	♄ St
10 Sat	♍ 20ʰ			H/E	Fruit to 19ʰ / Root 20ʰ	S
11 Sun	♍	♌11ʰ **Ag** 13ʰ ●☿		E	Root to 5ʰ / Fruit from 14ʰ	S
12 Mon	♍	▲		E	Fr -3ʰ / Root from 4ʰ	♄ St
13 Tue	♍	● 0ʰ		E	Root	
14 Wed	♎ 17ʰ			E/L	Root to 16ʰ / Flower 17ʰ	
15 Thu	♎			L	Flower to 15ʰ / Fruit from 16ʰ	♄ St
16 Fri	♏ 5ʰ		▲	L/W	Fruit to 7ʰ / Leaf from 8ʰ	St Eq
17 Sat	♏			W	Leaf	
18 Sun	♐ 17ʰ	☋ 18ʰ		W/H	Leaf to 16ʰ / Fruit from 17ʰ	
19 Mon	♐			H	Fruit	
20 Tue	♐	☽ 21ʰ		H	Fruit to 23ʰ	
21 Wed	♑ 0ʰ			E	Root from 0ʰ	St
22 Thu	♑			E	Root to 23ʰ	♄ St Eq Vo
23 Fri	♒ 0ʰ		▲	L	Fruit from 0ʰ to 11ʰ / Flower from 12ʰ	
24 Sat	♓ 17ʰ			L/W	Flower to 16ʰ / Leaf from 17ʰ	St
DST ends in Europe (incl UK and Ireland)						
25 Sun	♓	☊ 8ʰ		W	1ʰ	
26 Mon	♓	**Pg** 13ʰ ♀♌ ●⚷		W		St
27 Tue	♈ 6ʰ	○ 12ʰ		W/H	Lf 1ʰ - 5ʰ / Fruit from 6ʰ	
28 Wed	♉ 20ʰ			H/E	Fruit to 19ʰ / Root 20ʰ	St Eq
29 Thu	♉			E	Root	
30 Fri	♉			E	Root	St Tr
31 Sat	♊ 9ʰ	♑ 9ʰ		E/L	Root to 8ʰ / Flower from 9ʰ	
DST ends in North America						

Northern Transplanting Time (4–17)
Southern Transplanting Time (18–31)

0 1 2 3 4 5 6 7 8 9 10 11 12 13 14 15 16 17 18 19 20 21 22 23 24

Mercury ☿ ♍ (R, 9 D)	Venus ♀ ♌	Mars ♂ ♌	Jupiter ♃ ♌	Saturn ♄ ♏	Uranus ⚷ ♓ (R)	Neptune ♆ ♒ (R)	Pluto ♇ ♐

NB: All zodiac symbols refer to astronomical constellations, not astrological signs (see p.10

Planetary aspects

(Bold = *visible to naked eye*)

1 ☾ ☍ ♄ 22ʰ
2
3

4
5 ☾ ☍ ♇ 0ʰ
6
7 ♂ ☍ ♅ 3ʰ
8 ☿ ♌ 3ʰ ☾ ☍ ♀ 20ʰ
9 ☾ ☍ ♅ 11ʰ ☾ ☌ ♂ 14ʰ ☾ ☌ ♃ 21ʰ
10

11 ☾ ☌ ☿ 11ʰ
12 ♃ △ ♇ 0ʰ ☉ ☍ ♁ 4ʰ ☾ ☍ ♁ 22ʰ
13
14
15
16 ♂ △ ♇ 4ʰ ☽ ☌ ♄ 14ʰ
17 ♀ ☍ ♅ 3ʰ ♂ ☌ ♃ 23ʰ

18
19 ☽ ☌ ♇ 19ʰ
20
21
22
23 ♀ △ ♇ 8ʰ ☽ ☌ ♅ 17ʰ
24 ☽ ☍ ♀ 5ʰ ☽ ☍ ♃ 7ʰ ☽ ☍ ♂ 11ʰ

25 ♀ ☌ ♃ 20ʰ ☿ ☍ ♁ 23ʰ
26 ♀ ♌ 9ʰ ☽ ☌ ♁ 11ʰ ☽ ☍ ☿ 12ʰ
27
28
29 ☾ ☍ ♄ 13ʰ
30 ☉ △ ♅ 21ʰ
31

Planet (naked eye) visibility
Evening: Saturn
All night:
Morning: Venus, Mars, Jupiter, Mercury (6th to 26th, SH)

October 2015

Autumn has come. The Sun and Mercury are in the cool constellation of Virgo for the whole month. But Venus, Mars and Jupiter in Leo together with Pluto in Sagittarius may bring fine, warm days, supported by three Warmth trines on Oct 12, 16 and 23. Saturn in Scorpio and Uranus retrograde in Pisces may give rise to precipitation. Only Neptune works strongly in retrograde brings Light influences from Aquarius.

Northern Transplanting Time
Oct 4 0ʰ to Oct 18 17ʰ
and Oct 31 10ʰ to Nov 14
Southern Transplanting Time
Sep 21 to Oct 3 22ʰ and
Oct 18 20ʰ to Oct 31 6ʰ

Store fruit at any Fruit or Flower time outside transplanting time. A particularly favourable time is during Fruit trines (Oct 11 14ʰ to Oct 12 3ʰ, Oct 15 16ʰ to Oct 16 7ʰ, and Oct 23 0ʰ to 11ʰ).

Harvest seeds of root plants at Root times, **seeds for leaf plants** at Leaf times, and **seeds for flower plants** at Flower times.

All **cleared ground** should be treated with compost and sprayed with barrel preparation, and ploughed ready for winter.

Slug control from Oct 6 4ʰ to Oct 7 20ʰ.

Biodynamic preparations: Cut maple, fill with dandelion and put into the earth from Oct 11 22ʰ to Oct 12 11ʰ. Cut birch fill with yarrow and put into the earth from Oct 11 12ʰ to Oct 12 4ʰ.

Oct

November 2015

All times in GMT

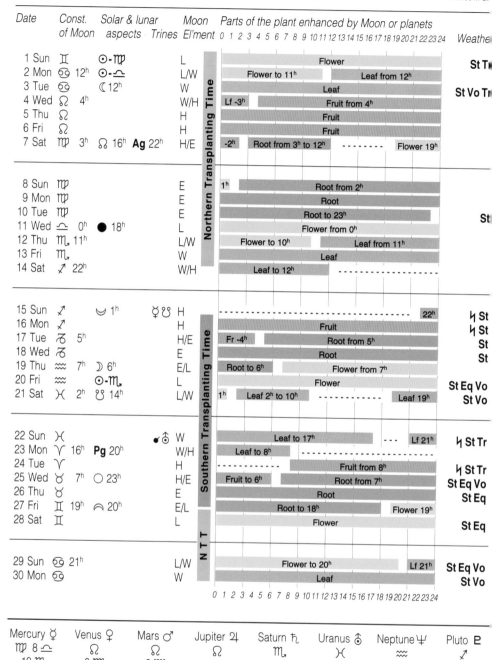

Date	Const. of Moon	Solar & lunar aspects	Trines	Moon El'ment	Parts of the plant enhanced by Moon or planets	Weather
1 Sun	♊	☉-♍		L	Flower	St Tr
2 Mon	♋ 12ʰ	☉-♎		L/W	Flower to 11ʰ · Leaf from 12ʰ	
3 Tue	♋	☾ 12ʰ		W	Leaf	St Vo Tr
4 Wed	♌ 4ʰ			W/H	Lf -3ʰ · Fruit from 4ʰ	
5 Thu	♌			H	Fruit	
6 Fri	♌			H	Fruit	
7 Sat	♍ 3ʰ	♌ 16ʰ **Ag** 22ʰ		H/E	-2ʰ · Root from 3ʰ to 12ʰ · Flower 19ʰ	
8 Sun	♍			E	1ʰ · Root from 2ʰ	
9 Mon	♍			E	Root	
10 Tue	♍			E	Root to 23ʰ	
11 Wed	♎ 0ʰ	● 18ʰ		L	Flower from 0ʰ	St
12 Thu	♏ 11ʰ			L/W	Flower to 10ʰ · Leaf from 11ʰ	
13 Fri	♏			W	Leaf	
14 Sat	♐ 22ʰ			W/H	Leaf to 12ʰ	
15 Sun	♐	☿ 1ʰ	☿ ♋	H	22ʰ	♄ St
16 Mon	♐			H	Fruit	♄ St
17 Tue	♑ 5ʰ			H/E	Fr -4ʰ · Root from 5ʰ	St
18 Wed	♑			E	Root	St
19 Thu	♒ 7ʰ	☽ 6ʰ		E/L	Root to 6ʰ · Flower from 7ʰ	
20 Fri	♒	☉-♏		L	Flower	St Eq Vo
21 Sat	♓ 2ʰ	♋ 14ʰ		L/W	1ʰ · Leaf 2ʰ to 10ʰ · Leaf 19ʰ	St Vo
22 Sun	♓	☽ ♄		W	Leaf to 17ʰ · Lf 21ʰ	♄ St Tr
23 Mon	♈ 16ʰ	**Pg** 20ʰ		W/H	Leaf to 8ʰ	
24 Tue	♈			H	Fruit from 8ʰ	♄ St Tr
25 Wed	♉ 7ʰ	○ 23ʰ		H/E	Fruit to 6ʰ · Root from 7ʰ	St Eq Vo
26 Thu	♉			E	Root	St Eq
27 Fri	♊ 19ʰ	⩘ 20ʰ		E/L	Root to 18ʰ · Flower 19ʰ	
28 Sat	♊			L	Flower	St Eq
29 Sun	♋ 21ʰ			L/W	Flower to 20ʰ · Lf 21ʰ	St Eq Vo
30 Mon	♋			W	Leaf	St Vo

Northern Transplanting Time — *Southern Transplanting Time* — *NTT*

Mercury ☿	Venus ♀	Mars ♂	Jupiter ♃	Saturn ♄	Uranus ♅	Neptune ♆	Pluto ♇
♍ 8 ♎	♌	♌	♌	♏	♓	♒	♐
19 ♏	2 ♍	2 ♍			(R)	(R, 18 D)	

38

NB: All zodiac symbols refer to astronomical constellations, not astrological signs (see p.10)

lanetary aspects
  (Bold = *visible to naked eye*)

1 ☾☌♇ 9^h
2
3 ♀☌♂ 1^h
4
5 ☾☌♆ 17^h
6 **☾☌♃ 14^h** ☿△♆ 14^h
7 **☾☌♂ 8^h** ☾☌♀ 13^h

8
9 ☾☌⊕ 3^h
0
1 ☾☌☿ 10^h
2
3 ☽☌♄ 2^h
4

5 ☿⯈ 10^h
6 ☽☌♇ 2^h
7 ☉☌☿ 15^h
8
9
0 ☽☌♆ 0^h ☽☌♃ 22^h
1

22 ☽☌♂ 0^h ☽☌♀ 17^h ☽•⊕ 19^h
23 ♀☌⊕ 22^h
24
25 ☿☌♄ 5^h
26 ☾☌♄ 5^h ☾☌☿ 7^h
27
28 ☾☌♇ 20^h

29
30 ☉☌♄ 0^h

Planet (naked eye) visibility
Evening: Saturn (to 10th)
All night:
Morning: Venus, Mars, Jupiter

November 2015

In the darkness of November there is still hope for some Light impulses in the first half of the month. Libra welcomes the Sun from Nov 2 to 20 and Mercury from Nov 8 to 19, and Neptune is in Aquarius. Venus and Mars begin the month in Leo, but on Nov 2 move to cool Virgo. Saturn is in watery Scorpio where Mercury and the Sun join Saturn on Nov 19 and 20. Uranus (retrograde in Pisces) reinforces precipitation which may come as rain or snow. Pluto and Jupiter in Sagittarius and Leo may still bring a little warmth.

Northern Transplanting Time
Oct 31 to Nov 14 12^h and
Nov 27 21^h to Dec12
Southern Transplanting Time
Nov 15 22^h to Nov 27 19^h

The Flower times in Transplanting Time (from Oct 31 9^h to Nov 2 11^h, from Nov 11 0^h to Nov 12 10^h) are ideal for **planting flower bulbs,** showing vigorous growth and vivid colours. The remaining Flower times should only be considered as back up, as bulbs planted on those times will not flower so freely.

If not already completed in October, all organic waste materials should be gathered and made into a **compost.** Applying the biodynamic preparations to the compost will ensure a rapid transformation and good fungal development. An application of barrel preparation will also help the composting process.

Fruit and forest trees will also benefit at this time from a spraying of horn manure and/or barrel preparation when being transplanted.

Best times for **cutting Advent greenery** and **Christmas trees** for transporting are Nov 19 7^h to Nov 21 1^h.

Burn **fly papers** in cow barn at Flower times.

NOV

December 2015

All times in GM

Date	Const. of Moon	Solar & lunar aspects	Trines	Moon El'ment	Parts of the plant enhanced by Moon or planets 0 1 2 3 4 5 6 7 8 9 10 11 12 13 14 15 16 17 18 19 20 21 22 23 24	Weather

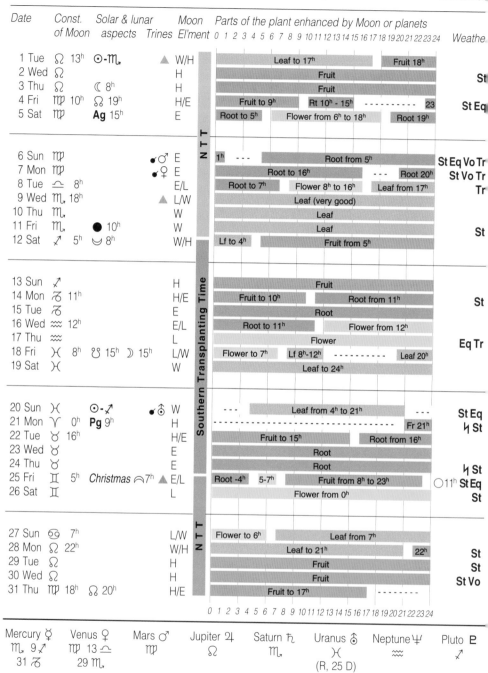

- 1 Tue ♌ 13ʰ ☉-♏ ▲ W/H — Leaf to 17ʰ / Fruit 18ʰ
- 2 Wed ♌ H — Fruit — St
- 3 Thu ♌ ☾ 8ʰ H — Fruit
- 4 Fri ♍ 10ʰ ♌ 19ʰ H/E — Fruit to 9ʰ / Rt 10ʰ - 15ʰ - - - - - - - - - - 23 — St Eq
- 5 Sat ♍ Ag 15ʰ E — Root to 5ʰ / Flower from 6ʰ to 18ʰ / Root 19ʰ

NTT

- 6 Sun ♍ ✦♂ E 1ʰ - - - Root from 5ʰ — St Eq Vo Tr
- 7 Mon ♍ ✦♀ E — Root to 16ʰ - - - Root 20ʰ — St Vo Tr
- 8 Tue ♎ 8ʰ E/L — Root to 7ʰ / Flower 8ʰ to 16ʰ / Leaf from 17ʰ — Tr
- 9 Wed ♏ 18ʰ ▲ L/W — Leaf (very good)
- 10 Thu ♏ W — Leaf
- 11 Fri ♏ ● 10ʰ W — Leaf — St
- 12 Sat ♐ 5ʰ ☋ 8ʰ W/H — Lf to 4ʰ / Fruit from 5ʰ

Southern Transplanting Time

- 13 Sun ♐ H — Fruit
- 14 Mon ♑ 11ʰ H/E — Fruit to 10ʰ / Root from 11ʰ — St
- 15 Tue ♑ E — Root
- 16 Wed ♒ 12ʰ E/L — Root to 11ʰ / Flower from 12ʰ
- 17 Thu ♒ L — Flower — Eq Tr
- 18 Fri ♓ 8ʰ ☊ 15ʰ ☽ 15ʰ L/W — Flower to 7ʰ / Lf 8ʰ-12ʰ - - - - - - - - Leaf 20ʰ
- 19 Sat ♓ W — Leaf to 24ʰ

- 20 Sun ♓ ☉-♐ ✦⛢ W — - - - Leaf from 4ʰ to 21ʰ - - - — St Eq
- 21 Mon ♈ 0ʰ Pg 9ʰ H — - - - - - - - - - - - - - - - - - - - Fr 21ʰ — ♄ St
- 22 Tue ♉ 16ʰ H/E — Fruit to 15ʰ / Root from 16ʰ
- 23 Wed ♉ E — Root
- 24 Thu ♉ E — Root — ♄ St
- 25 Fri ♊ 5ʰ Christmas ⌢7ʰ ▲ E/L — Root -4ʰ / 5-7ʰ / Fruit from 8ʰ to 23ʰ — ○11ʰ St Eq
- 26 Sat ♊ L — Flower from 0ʰ — St

NTT

- 27 Sun ♋ 7ʰ L/W — Flower to 6ʰ / Leaf from 7ʰ
- 28 Mon ♌ 22ʰ W/H — Leaf to 21ʰ 22ʰ — St
- 29 Tue ♌ H — Fruit — St
- 30 Wed ♌ H — Fruit — St Vo
- 31 Thu ♍ 18ʰ ♌ 20ʰ H/E — Fruit to 17ʰ - - - - - - - -

0 1 2 3 4 5 6 7 8 9 10 11 12 13 14 15 16 17 18 19 20 21 22 23 24

Mercury ☿	Venus ♀	Mars ♂	Jupiter ♃	Saturn ♄	Uranus ⛢	Neptune ♆	Pluto ♇
♏ 9 ♐	♍ 13 ♎	♍	♌	♏	♓	♒	♐
31 ♑	29 ♏				(R, 25 D)		

NB: All zodiac symbols refer to astronomical constellations, not astrological signs (see p.10)

Planetary aspects
(Bold = visible to naked eye)

1 $\lightning \triangle \hat{\oplus}$ 14^h
2
3 $\mathbb{C} \sigma^o \Psi$ 0^h
4 **$\mathbb{C} \sigma 2\!\!\!\downarrow$ 5^h**
5

6 **$\mathbb{C} \bullet \sigma^o$ 3^h** $\mathbb{C} \sigma^o \hat{\oplus}$ 9^h
7 **$\mathbb{C} \bullet \female$ 17^h**
8
9 $\odot \triangle \hat{\oplus}$ 2^h
10 $\mathbb{C} \sigma \hbar$ 15^h
11 $\sigma^o \sigma^o \hat{\oplus}$ 2^h $\female \triangle \Psi$ 6^h
12 $\mathbb{D} \sigma \lightning$ 14^h

13 $\mathbb{D} \sigma \mathbb{P}$ 9^h
14
15
16
17 $\mathbb{D} \sigma \Psi$ 6^h
18 $\mathbb{D} \sigma^o 2\!\!\!\downarrow$ 9^h
19 $\lightning \sigma \mathbb{P}$ 19^h

20 $\mathbb{D} \bullet \hat{\oplus}$ 2^h $\mathbb{D} \sigma^o \sigma^o$ 11^h
21
22 $\mathbb{D} \sigma^o \female$ 11^h
23 $\mathbb{D} \sigma^o \hbar$ 20^h
24
25 $\lightning \triangle 2\!\!\!\downarrow$ 20^h
26 $\mathbb{C} \sigma^o \mathbb{P}$ 7^h

27 $\mathbb{C} \sigma^o \lightning$ 0^h
28
29
30 $\mathbb{C} \sigma^o \Psi$ 10^h
31 **$\mathbb{C} \sigma 2\!\!\!\downarrow$ 17^h**

Planet (naked eye) visibility
Evening: Mercury (from 21st)
All night: Jupiter
Morning: Venus, Mars, Saturn (from 18th)

December 2015

Until Dec 20 the Sun is in watery Scorpio. Mercury begins the month and Venus ends the month also in Scorpio, where Saturn remains all month. The Sun moves on to the Warmth constellation of Sagittarius on Dec 20. Pluto in Sagittarius and Jupiter in Leo bring Warmth influences throughout the month, with a Warmth trine on Christmas Day.

Mars remains in the cool Earth constellation of Virgo throughout the month. Briefly Venus visits Libra from Dec 13 to 29, and with Neptune in Aquarius they bring Light influences, perhaps sunny winter days.

Northern Transplanting Time
Nov 27 to Dec 12 7^h and Dec 25 9^h to Jan 8
Southern Transplanting Time
Dec 12 10^h to Dec 25 6^h

The transplanting time is good for **pruning trees and hedges.** Fruit trees should be pruned at Fruit times.

Best times for cutting **Advent greenery** and **Christmas trees** are at Flower times to ensure lasting fragrance.

Southern hemisphere:
Control slugs Nov 29 21^h to Dec 1 12^h, and Dec 27 7^h to Dec 28 21^h.
Harvest time for seeds:
Leaf seeds: Leaf times.
Fruit seeds: Fruit times, preferably with Moon in Leo (Dec 1 18^h to Dec 4 10^h, and Dec 28 22^h to Dec 31 17^h).
Root seeds: Root times.
Flower seeds: Flower times.

Biodynamic preparations: Cut oak, fill it with ground oak bark and put it in the earth between Dec 10 21^h and Dec 11 8^h.

*We would like to wish all our readers
a blessed Advent and Christmastide
and good health for the New Year of 2016*

41

Sowing times for trees and shrubs

Jan 19: Pear, Birch, Lime tree, Robinia, Willow

March 3: Apple, Beech, Ash, Sweet chestnut

April 2: Plum, Ash, Spruce, Hazel, Hornbeam, Fir, Cedar, Thuja, Plum

April 15: Pear, Birch, Oak, Yew, Lime tree, Robinia, Willow

May 3: Alder, Larch, Lime tree, Elm, Plum, Ash, Spruce, Hazel, Hornbeam, Fir, Cedar, Thuja, Plum

May 15: Yew, Oak, Ash, Spruce, Hazel, Fir, Pine, Horse chestnut (buckeye)

May 22: Pear, Birch, Lime tree, Robinia, Willow

May 23: Ash, Spruce, Hazel, Fir, Cedar

July 15: Alder, Yew, Oak, Larch, Lime tree, Elm, Cherry, Peach, Apricot

Sep 1: Ash, Spruce, Hazel, Fir, Cedar

Sep 17: Maple, Apple, Beech, Sweet chestnut

Oct 7: Yew, Oak, Sweet chestnut, Horse chestnut (buckeye), Cherry

Oct 12: Ash, Spruce, Hazel, Fir, Cedar

Nov 23: Pear, Birch, Lime tree, Robinia, Willow

The above dates refer to sowing times of the seeds. They are not times for transplanting already existing plants.

The dates given are based on planetary aspects, which create particularly favourable growing conditions for the species in question. For trees and shrubs not mentioned above, sow at an appropriate time of the Moon's position in the zodiac, depending on the part of the tree or shrub to be enhanced. Avoid unfavourable times.

Felling times for timber

Feb 24: Birch, Pear, Larch, Lime tree, Robinia, Willow

Feb 26: Apple, Beech, Ash, Spruce, Hazel, Sweet chestnut

March 4: Birch, Pear, Robinia

April 2: Ash, Spruce, Hazel, Cherry, Fir, Cedar

April 6: Alder, Larch, Lime tree, Sweet chestnut, Elm

April 21: Apple, Larch, Lime tree, Pine, Sweet chestnut, Horse chestnut (buckeye)

June 29: Birch, Pear, Robinia, Willow

July 1: Ash, Spruce, Hazel, Fir, Cedar

July 7: Alder, Yew, Oak, Cherry, Larch, Lime tree

July 22: Alder, Yew, Oak, Cherry, Larch, Lime tree, Apricot, Peach

Aug 2: Alder, Larch, Lime tree, Elm

Aug 13: Ash, Spruce, Fir, Cedar

Aug 19: Birch, Pear, Larch, Lime tree, Robinia, Willow

Sep 19: Birch, Pear, Robinia

Oct 16: Ash, Spruce, Sweet chestnut, Fir, Cedar

Oct 30: Ash, Spruce, Hazel, Fir, Cedar

Nov 6: Alder, Larch, Lime tree, Elm

Dec 1: Alder, Larch, Lime tree, Elm, Fir, Thuja, Elm, Juniper, Walnut

Dec 9: Ash, Spruce, Hornbeam, Hazel, Fir, Cedar

Those trees which are not listed should be felled during November and December at Flower times during the descending Moon period (transplanting time). Avoid unfavourable times (- - - -).

Fungal problems

The function of fungus in nature is to break down dying organic materials. It appears amongst our crops when unripe manure compost or uncomposted animal by-products such as horn and bone meal are used but also when seeds are harvested during unfavourable constellations: according to Steiner, 'When Moon forces are working too strongly on the Earth ...'

Tea can be made from horsetail *(Equisetum arvense)* and sprayed on to the soil where affected plants are growing. This draws the fungal level back down into the ground where it belongs.

The plants can be strengthened by spraying stinging nettle tea on the leaves. This will promote good assimilation, stimulate the flow of sap and help fungal diseases to disappear.

Biodynamic preparation plants

Pick **dandelions** in the morning at Flower times as soon as they are open and while the centre of the flowers are still tightly packed.

Pick **yarrow** at Fruit times when the Sun is in Leo (around middle of August).

Pick **chamomile** at Flower times just before midsummer. If they are harvested too late, seeds will begin to form and there are often grubs in the hollow heads.

Collect **stinging nettles** when the first flowers are opening, usually around midsummer. Harvest the whole plants without roots at Flower times.

Pick **valerian** at Flower times around midsummer. All the flowers (except valerian) should be laid out on paper and dried in the shade.

Collect **oak bark** at Root times. The pithy material below the bark should not be used.

The care of bees

A colony of bees lives in its hive closed off from the outside world. For extra protection against harmful influences, the inside of the hive is sealed with propolis. The link with the wider surroundings is made by the bees which fly in and out of the hive.

To make good use of cosmic rhythms, the beekeeper needs to create the right conditions in much the same way as the gardener or farmer does with the plants. The gardener works the soil and in so doing allows cosmic forces to penetrate it via the air. These forces can then be taken up and used by the plants until the soil is next moved.

When the beekeeper opens up the hive, the sealing layer of propolis is broken. This creates a disturbance as a result of which cosmic forces can enter and influence the life of the hive until the next intervention by the beekeeper. By this means the beekeeper can directly mediate cosmic forces to the bees.

It is not insignificant which forces of the universe are brought into play when the the the hive is opened. The beekeeper can consciously intervene by choosing days for working with the hive that will help the colony to develop and build up its food reserves. The bees will then reward the beekeeper by providing a portion of their harvest in the form of honey.

Earth-Root times can be selected for opening the hive if the bees need to do more building. Light-Flower times encourage brood activity and colony development. Warmth-Fruit times stimulate the collection of nectar. Water-Leaf times are unsuitable for working in the hive or for the removal and processing of honey.

Since the late 1970s the varroa mite has affected virtually every bee colony in Europe. Following a number of comparative trials we recommend burning and making an ash of the varroa mite in the usual way. After dynamizing it for one hour, the ash should be put in a salt-cellar and sprinkled lightly between the combs. The ash should be made and sprinkled when the Sun and Moon are in Taurus (May/June).

Feeding bees in preparation for winter

The herbal teas recommended as supplements in the feeding of bees prior to winter are all plants that have proved their value over many years. Yarrow, chamomile, dandelion and valerian are made by pouring boiling water over the flowers, allowing them to brew for fifteen minutes and then straining them. Stinging nettle, horsetail and oak bark are placed in cold water, brought slowly to the boil and simmered for fifteen minutes. Three grams (1 tablespoon) of each dried herb and half a litre (quart) of the prepared teas is enough to produce 100 litres (25 gal) of liquid feed. This is a particularly important treatment in years when there are large amounts of honeydew.

Recipe for rye bread

Since all the grains we grow in our experiments were tested for quality, we have used our own raising agents (without additives) for bread baking to produce a good loaf. Besides sour milk, buttermilk, whey and syrup we have also tried to bake with honey and have developed a recipe that has proved its worth over many years.

To make 2 large loafs, use 2 kg (4 lb) of rye flour.

One heaped teaspoon of flower honey is stirred well in a glass of warm water (50°C, 120°F) and then mixed with 125 g (¼ lb) of finely-ground rye flour. This small amount of dough is made in the evening and kept warm overnight to allow it to rise for the first time. It should be at a temperature of about 26–30°C (80–85°F) by the stove or next to a hot plate, which is set very low. Next morning add the same amount of rye flour and warm water or whey and allow to rise for the second time.

In the evening add just over 1 kg (2 lb) of the flour to the prepared dough with sufficient warm water. At this stage you can add a little linseed, caraway, fennel or something similar. After mixing in these herbs, add the rest of the flour. Leave it to rise overnight for the third

time. Next morning add salt and knead the dough. When it begins to rise for the fourth time the dough is ready.

Put some finished dough aside to use use as a starter for next time. Shape the loaves, let them rise well, put them in a preheated oven (150°C, 300°F). After ten minutes increase the temperature to 200°C (390°F), and bake them for another 50 minutes. Check the loaves, as every oven is a bit different, the time may vary. Rye is easy to digest when it has gone through these five stages.

Keep the starter in an earthenware pot. After it has risen again a little, sprinkle with salt, cover with greaseproof paper and store in a cool place (not the fridge). When you want to do some more baking, take the pot from the cool place in the morning and add a teaspoon of honey, which has been stirred in a glass of warm water. Then keep the pot warm. In the evening you can start on the main dough and proceed as described above.

Traditionally after 40 days, the starter was no longer used, and the process was started from stage one again.

Rye should rise five times. Wheat, barley and oats need to rise only three steps. Success depends on the warmth of the baking area.

Eggshells

To add flavour to bread we can add caraway, linseed, fennel, sunflower seeds and the like to the dough. These not only increase the flavour but make digestion easier. Through our digestion the different forces and influences of these substances reach all parts of our body through our bloodstream.

Over the years there has been an increase in osteoarthritis and other stiffness and pain of the joints like periostitis, the inflammation of the outer layer of connective tissue surrounding the bone. Maria Thun wondered which substances might help the health of bones and joint.

In the 1960s and 70s, while developing the Barrel Preparation, she made an intensive study of calcium and lime. This involved a number of trials with eggshells of hens, geese, ducks, ostriches, and snail shells. It was then she came across the eggshell membrane, which is the clear lining inside the shell surrounding the egg white. The eggshells consist primarily of calcium and the eggshell membrane of silica. But this calcium and silica substance originates in an animal organism and has quite a different character and influence to mineral calcium and silica.

The trials with eggshells showed that hen's eggs were the most versatile. From her many years of studying the spiritual evolution of human beings, Maria Thun suggested that those suffering from joint complaints should eat eggshells. The calcium shell works on the bone structure, and the membrane on the periosteum (the outer layer of the bone). This was shown to be successful in many cases.

Now the question was how best to

Eggshells and membrane

Muesli with ground eggshells

consume eggshells. Use your own hen's eggs or organic eggs. After breaking an egg, ensure the egg white and yolk are all removed, and allow the eggshell and membrane to dry. Break them finely by hand, and grind them coarsely in a coffee grinder so they resemble coarse meal. Add about half a tablespoon of this eggshell grist to 1 kg (2 lb) of dough and knead well.

If you do not bake bread yourself, add about a teaspoon of the eggshell grit to your breakfast muesli or cereal. Mix it well, and you hardly notice the eggshells when chewing.

Sowing and transplanting on Good Friday and Easter Saturday

Again and again we are asked by readers why no sowing or other cultivations should be undertaken on Good Friday and Easter Saturday.

Maria Thun grew up on a small farm managed by her parents. They were deeply embedded in the Christian faith and strongly believed that no work apart from the daily care of animals should be carried out on such festival days. It was also said that plants sown and cultivated on those days would not thrive because God the Father could not fully attend to them while his Son was being crucified on Good Friday. It was therefore a strongly held belief that God took care of the way plants grew. Maria Thun could not let this idea rest. After she had undertaken many planting trials that showed how the Moon and planets can affect plant growth, she decided to investigate the mystery of Good Friday with specific planting trials.

Comparative sowings were then undertaken, beginning a few days before Good Friday and ending a few days after Easter Sunday. Because in the early years many of the sowings were carried out by hand and there was direct contact between human being and seed, some readers suggested that this direct contact might influence the plants and affect the results. In order to minimise this direct contact or even prevent it, the sowings were increasingly carried out by machine and not by Maria Thun directly.

These Good Friday sowings were repeated each year into the 1980s. Results were always similar. Beans, radishes, spinach and lettuce were chosen as test plants. A spring sown cereal was also included but only if Easter was early. Regardless of the lunar constellations or planetary aspects, some of the plants germinated well but then didn't develop properly, while other seedlings were so weak that no worthwhile crop could be expected.

It is as though nature holds its breath between Good Friday and Easter Sunday and that the event of Easter Sunday brings renewed vitality to living organisms. These observations led us to recommend avoiding this period in the calendar.

Controlling slugs

Slugs appear in crops and plants causing problems for farmers and gardeners. They are known to all growers, as they have a particular love of lettuce, vegetables and even flower seedlings. In some years they even infest rapeseed plants at an early stage.

We are repeatedly asked what can be done to combat this deluge of slugs.

Over the years it was observed, for instance in rapeseed fields in autumn or with vegetables in spring, that slugs seemed happiest and multiplied during times when the Moon was in Water constellations. The type of soil also makes a difference – limestone soils have more slugs than sandy or granite soils. Soils which tend to become muddy after rains are more affected by slugs.

Crop rotation or green manuring can also make things worse if used carelessly. Green manure needs to be well mulched, chaffed or cut. Let it dry a bit, more than just wilting so that the chlorophyll begins to dissolve. That is helpful during further rotting as worms can only digest cellulose which no longer contains chlorophyll. If green manure is applied directly, depending on the type of soil, it will take much longer to rot and can easily become mouldy. This forms delightful conditions for slugs.

Unfortunately various experts recommend covering vegetable beds to prevent the soil drying. Many small gardens and nurseries spread grass cuttings which do not compost well and may lead to mould. They keep the soil damp and eventually dry sufficiently to rot. This is the good side – but if there is a rainy time the conditions under the grass cuttings are ideal for slugs, creating a veritable slug paradise.

Slug with eggs

Collected slugs in a jar

A more positive approach is hoeing. oeing in the morning dries the soil as it reathes out then. Hoeing in the evenings ill make it moist as it breathes in the ightly dew. A side effect is that in agiating the soil, air – that is, oxygen and itrogen – enters and is absorbed by the icroorganisms of the soil. Thus, not only in the moisture of the beds be regulated, ut a free organic nitrogen fertiliser is pplied. This is something which slugs eally do not like!

Raised beds could become a thriving nvironment for slugs. Raised beds were a it of a craze. They help domestic gardenrs with back problems to attend to their lants. To save on good topsoil when fillg the raised beds which were enclosed 1 wooden boards, stones or bricks, they rere partly filled with chopped branches r plant matter and then covered in soil. his worked quite well if one ignored the igh nitrate content of the plants. Howver, when anything was sown in these eds, it sprouted and then mysteriously isappeared. Usually tiny black slugs rere the culprits who ate the seedlings vernight. So raised beds are perhaps not lways ideal.

So what measures can be taken gainst slugs?

The following suggestions may not ppeal to every reader. We have seen, owever, that it is often human intervenion that has enabled slugs to have such field day. So we should perhaps ask urselves whether we are growing things s food for slugs or for humans.

Making slug slurry

Slug slurry

The simplest of course is to collect the slugs, but what do we do with them? Just throwing them into the neighbour's garden is neither helpful nor does it stop them coming back. Other people cut the slugs, cover them in salt, catch them in beer traps, or use slug pellets. These methods may not be very humane.

After many trials to find how not to kill off the slugs but to change the ambience around our crops and vegetables so that slugs are no longer attracted there, we came to various conclusions.

Collect slugs in a jar with a lid for two or three days. Then transfer them to a larger jar filled with water. Keep airtight. After about a week you have slug slurry which has a strong smell. To lessen the smell dilute the slurry in a bucket of water and stir well. Filter through a fine sieve and spray the beds (not the plants) with a hand-sprayer or backpack spray. This is best done when the Moon is in Cancer.

Slug ash

A more cumbersome but very effective method is to use slug ash. Again collect some slugs in a jar with a lid. After one or two days put them in an egg carton and burn them to ash.

Do this on a wood fire. Oil, electric or charcoal are not suitable. Use dry wood that produces embers that glow for a long time. Once there is a bright red glow, tip the slugs out of the egg container onto the embers. Cover the fire with a lid, or if done in a wood-burning stove, close off the flue to ensure the slugs are properly incinerated. A garden grill pan can also be used provided wood is used and not charcoal.

Once the embers have died down the ash should be light grey, not black. Sieve the ash and grind with a pestle in a mor-

tar for an hour. This is the dynamisin process. The mortar should be porcelai or glass, not metal or synthetic. The as thus ground is the base substance.

The base substance can now be pe pered over the affected ground with pepp shaker or similar. But as usually the is too little ash to pepper the entire are required, we can borrow from homeopath and create a D8 dilution. This appears enhance most ashes to greatest efficacy.

To make a dilution, one part bas material is mixed with nine parts dilutin substance. The diluting substance can t either ash or water.

Potentising with ash

Put 9 parts pure wood ash into a morta and add 1 part base substance. (Alway start with the diluting substance.) Th can be measured by weight or by volum If you don't have a suitable measurin flask, use a thimble or an egg cup.

Mix and grind for 3 minutes. Th makes D1 dilution. Then take 90 part of pure wood ash and add 10 parts of D

Slugs in an egg carton to be incinerated

Close the lid of the grill pan when making as

light coloured ash

nd grind again for 3 minutes to make)2. Dilute and grind again to make D3. Around D4 even a large mortar will be too mall. Take 9 parts ash and 1 part D4 and ontinue to D8. This is used for peppering he ground.

Keep the D3 or D4 ash not used. Put t in a jar and label it with potency (D3 or)4), type (slug) and date. With an airtight id it can be kept for several years to make iew potencies.

To help concentrate and remember at vhat stage we are, we have found it use-ul (if a little odd) to keep saying out loud, I'm making D1, I'm making D1 ..." and vhen it's complete to say, "I have finished)1." Then if we are interrupted by an inexpected visit or phone call, we tend to emember where we left off, because our ast sentence is still echoing in our ears.

The best times for making the ash are ndicated in the Calendar every year.

²otentising with water

'he procedure is similar if using water. 'o make D1 start with 9 parts water and idd one part base substance (ash) in a ¡lass, stone or clay container or an enam-elled bucket. Again always start with the diluting matter (water) and add the previous potency (or base substance when making D1) to it. (If you start with the previous potency and then add nine parts one after the other, this produces a new potency with each addition, preventing a pure new potency from being made.)

Stir the mixture allowing a vortex to form. Then change direction and allow a new vortex to form. Three minutes of stirring in total is needed for making each potency. As the amounts get larger a wooden barrel may be used for stirring. It can again help to repeat aloud the stage one is at in case of interruptions.

Once D8 is made, this is used to spray the ground with a hand-sprayer or back-pack spray.

While it all sounds quite complicated, it becomes easier and quicker the second or third time.

Horn silica preparation

Another method of combating snails is to use quartz (siliceous) sand. Some green-house growers spread some pure quartz sand between lettuce or vegetable plants. The theory is that slugs will injure them-selves on the sharp edges of the sand. In practice any improvement is short-lived.

In biodynamic farming horn silica (501) is used. This preparation is really meant to stimulate plant growth, but also reduces slugs.

The downside, if it is to combat slugs, is that it needs to be stirred for an hour at dawn at Flower times before being sprayed. Stirring must be for 60 min-utes – at 55 it has not yet reached its

Quantity of preparation 501 for 15 litres (4 gal)

Stirring the horn silica preparation

full efficacy, and at 65 minutes its power diminishes. Once stirred the preparation will be usable for about 3 or 4 hours before losing strength. To combat slugs, spray onto the soil around the plants. If bio-dynamic rapeseed has a slug problem it will be during the early phase of growth when the plants need to be sprayed in the early morning with horn silica anyway.

Stirring (or dynamising) is done in the same way as the dilution described above. Stir in one direction until a good vortex is formed; then stir in the other direction until a new vortex is formed. Each time the vortex should be as deep as possible.

These various possibilities show that we need to try and fully understand the nature of slugs and their way of life. This will help us find a solution for our particular situation. •

Controlling Colorado beetle

As Colorado beetle is widespread we shall describe a method of combating it.

The trials of the 1960s showed that it can best be controlled in a similar way to slugs, by making slurry or by inciner-ating it. Spraying the plants will then make them unattractive to the beetle, so that it should not affect the potato plantation.

Collect Colorado beetles and their lar-vae and keep in a sealed jar until the right planetary aspects come for making ash. The dates will be found annually in the Calendar.

Now follow the same procedure as for incinerating slugs, making a beetle ash on a wood fire or in a grill pan using wood not charcoal. Make a D8 dilution as for slug ash.

Spray the potato plants using a back-pack sprayer. The plants should become really wet. This needs to be done three

Colorado beetle eating a potato

Making a slurry

Pouring the slurry before stirring

Slurry and beetles

Wood fire for incinerating

times about a week apart to ensure any eggs that hatch are also controlled.

Instead of incinerating, you can make slurry like for slugs. However, because of their chitinous wings and other parts it takes rather longer to produce. The potentised slurry works best if applied in spring onto the parcel of land to be planted. If you have plenty of potentised slurry you can spray it on the ground in autumn before preparing it for the winter.

Embers are ready for adding Colorado beetles

Sieving the beetle ash

Grinding in a pestle and mortar

Potentising the ash

54

From Gardeners and Growers in Slovenia

Some of the reports have had to be abridged for reasons of space.

Maria Thun's *Biodynamic Calendar* was my first meeting with biodynamic agriculture. Till then I knew only of anthroposophical medicine and the Waldorf kindergarten. Though both of these moved me deeply, it was the Calendar that changed my life. Growing up in Slovenia and then working as a translator in Stuttgart made me very aware of the harm industrialisation and modern agriculture was doing to nature and the human being. The discovery of an approach to agriculture that did not damage the environment yet produced high yielding crops of excellent quality was so important to me that I decided to devote myself to it and share this interest with my Slovenian compatriots.

That same summer in 1985 I visited Maria Thun in Dexbach. Dressed simply and wearing a headscarf tied at the back, she welcomed me and to my great surprise gave over an entire working day to me. Her home was filled with beautiful crystals and I can still remember vases that were filled with wonderful deep blue delphiniums. We spoke about my concerns and looked at her fields. She showed me her Osiris wheat and afterwards gave me three large ears to take home. I can recall counting 156 grains in one ear. I was invited to taste the strawberries she brought home in a bucket and then share a meal with goulash.

I drove back to Stuttgart in the evening with an agreement to publish at first sections and then the entire Calendar in Slovenian. I also intended to raise awareness for biodynamic agriculture in Slovenia by arranging as many lectures as possible.

That was the beginning.

In October 1985 my first article about this new approach to agriculture and the Moon calendar appeared in Slovenian newspapers, and in 1988 the first Slovenian edition of the Calendar. This was accompanied by many visits from Maria and Matthias Thun who gave lectures in various towns and villages across Slovenia. These were supported by the Slovenian amateur gardening association and received with great interest. From 1985 onward I attended as many lectures and conferences about biodynamic agriculture as I could manage, participated in the annual conference in Dornach, Switzerland, listened to remarkable presentations and invited many speakers to Slovenia.

In 1988 I bought a farm in Slovenia so that we could have a place on which to produce the biodynamic preparations. Here, in 1991 we founded the first Slovenian biodynamic association called AJDA (*ajda* is a Slovenian word meaning buckwheat).

Once the association's membership reached 700 we started regional working groups. Today there are 16 biodynamic associations in Slovenia with around 3,000 members. The aim is for them to disseminate this new knowledge in their immediate surroundings. The first Demeter producers were registered in 1997 and an independent Demeter certification initiative was established five years ago. Two years ago it became a full member of Demeter International.

When I started distributing the Calendar in Slovenia praise was not the only response I received. Some friends were of the opinion that the biodynamic method should only be practised by anthroposophists. To me however it was inconceivable not to pass on this knowledge at the earliest opportunity. And even if years later, most gardeners are still not anthroposophists and may indeed never be so in this life, the work they are doing is vital for the survival of the earth and our cultivated plants. There is also no doubt in my mind that the food produced in this way can help guide humanity in a new direction.

Margareta Vrhunc, a wine grower

Our work with biodynamic agriculture began in 1988. The working group of the AJDA Association was at that time led by Meta Vrhunc.

Our work would be unimaginable without the Calendar. Each new member receives a copy on joining the association. We also work together on the recommendations given in the Calendar. We plan days to collect the preparation plants, make the preparations, prepare materials to control pests and so forth. There are so many important indications given in the Calendar and for the association it is an exceptionally good tool for promoting the

work to people who are looking for natural growing methods. The Calendar is not only of novelty value but also engenders trust and can be put to successful use everywhere.

We are proud after sixteen years that alongside the many active biodynamic gardeners, we have some wine growers and several farmers and market gardeners some of whom are now Demeter certified.

We make the preparations together in the association and store them carefully. Stirring takes place in many places with groups of members. In this way the preparations gain wider use and create opportunities for strengthening friendships. We also make an effort to share the biodynamic approach with people in the surroundings.

Breda Medvescek, AJDA Goriska

The first copy of the Calendar came into my hands in 1990. I had felt my plants had been getting steadily weaker and so I sought help. The contents of the Calendar were entirely new for me. I decided that first of all I should try and consciously understand its contents and learn how to read the Calendar. At the same time I tried to make contact with people who were already practising this approach.

I did not wish to miss any of the activities arranged by the Biodynamic Association and despite the great distances involved, eagerly travelled to hear many of the lectures which Maria Thun gave in Slovenia. What I learnt through these lectures far exceeded my expectations and gave me not only the means

Making biodynamic preparations together

to bring new fertility to the earth and form a connection with the stars, it also gave meaning to my whole existence. An entirely new dimension opened up for me in the way I could work with the earth and my plants.

Shortly afterwards I obtained my first biodynamic preparations and could observe some positive changes brought about by observance of the Calendar and especially the frequent application of Barrel Preparation. My fields which had previously tended to be too wet and heavy or else in dry weather become as hard as concrete, now became light and crumbly. Yields increased significantly especially those of fruit bearing plants. The potatoes planted according to the Calendar no longer went rotten. Our fruit and vegetables developed a wonderful flavour. On the advice of Maria Thun we sprayed our meadows with Barrel Preparation immediately after cutting and then when the new grass had grown about 10 cm (4 in) sprayed it with horn silica. The hay smelled wonderful and our animals have become more healthy. Many more herbs and quality grasses have started to appear in the meadows and pastures which have also become havens for bees and other beneficial insects.

Marija Poljanec, Chair of AJDA Posočje

The Calendar has its place on a rustic chest in our living room. It is always open and symbolises both peace and creative power. This is similar to the way the old Venetian coat of arms was understood: a closed book meant war or even death.

For me the Biodynamic Calendar is a source of ancient wisdom imprinted in the stars and planetary constellations to nourish all life on earth. It is my assistant. With its help I am empowered to work as a farmer and wine grower with the forces of the cosmos.

And how does my vineyard respond? During transplanting times, in descending Moon periods, my vines are less affected by mildew. I can rely on this. My vineyard needs more care and attention during the ascending Moon.

Aci Urbajs making music in the vineyard and in the wine cellar

A special part of my winemaking approach is that I use no sulphur. Instead I make music for my wine in the cellar. This is particularly effective if carried out at Light or Warmth times or when there are Light or Warmth trines. The musical resonance produced in this way has such a calming and beneficial effect on my wine that no sulphur is needed. I am using forces from the cosmos to improve the quality of my wine.

It is similar with the preparations and teas used in my vineyard and which I apply exactly according to Maria Thun's recommendations. The days for stirring are carefully chosen using the Calendar and I then infuse the stirred preparation or tea with music. My imagination is that by doing this I am able permeate the water, which after all mediates between heaven and earth, with something of my own nature.

Aci Urbajs, Demeter wine grower

I came across the Calendar and the biodynamic approach ten years ago. To begin with it felt as if I were returning to my childhood. In those days I remember how we used to cultivate the land entirely without artificial fertilisers and poisons.

It is wonderful to realise today how through this approach we can connect to the earth and the cosmos in an open, loving and childlike way knowing that everyone and not only children can do so. The Calendar inspires me to try and observe what occurs in nature, understand her inner laws and processes and thereby experience the world as something truly alive. It is amazing how many possibilities can be found for advancing human culture by engaging with the contents of the Calendar and how by inwardly connecting with them we can become agents of change. It is also moving to discover how nature herself changes as we work and develop.

Nature's appreciation for my activity became visible to me when I discovered wild centaury *(Centaurium erythraea)* growing in my fields. I remember how as children we used to gather this medicinal plant on our fields and then how it van-

Working in the greenhouse

...shed for many decades. And now I have the joy of finding it on my farm.

I do a lot of work with herbs and if they are picked at Flower times they retain their flavour and aroma for many years. As a chemist I have no explanation for this. I often ask myself what is the secret that weaves light into the plants. Can it be likened to what goes on within me? My outer activity may change but it is my inner transformation that is more significant. For me it is only the biodynamic approach, carried out by human beings in partnership with the cosmos that can bring healing to the wounds inflicted on nature. And everything is filled with joy wherever this occurs – in plants, in the earth and in human beings.

Majda Temnik, chemist

I have used the Calendar for many years. I got to know about it at the end of the 1990s when my father became one of the first Demeter farmers in Slovenia. Now I am growing vegetables in the context of an agricultural cooperative. I started out by following the recommendations given in the Calendar as exactly as I could. It is of course not always practical to choose the most favourable days for sowing and cultivation. But we do stick to the recommendations wherever possible.

The effect of the constellations has been particularly noticeable in the storage of vegetables. Several years ago, for example, we had to harvest some of our potatoes at a Leaf time. Luckily most were done at a Root time. We found that those harvested at a Leaf time were sprouting by the end of December and were no longer usable. The rest of the potatoes kept well and retained their flavour until the end of May. The same held true for other root vegetables and onions.

I am also a professor of agriculture at the University of Maribor. I find that each year more and more students are interested in researching and testing the suggestions given in the Calendar. Several projects have also been carried out on the subject. The results have generally confirmed the Calendar's recommendations although in some cases the differences could not be measured. This does not of course mean that they weren't there.

Dr Matjaz Turinek, farmer & professor

Moon diagrams

The diagrams overleaf show for each month the daily position (evenings GMT) of the Moon against the stars and other planets. For viewing in the southern hemisphere, turn the diagrams upside down.

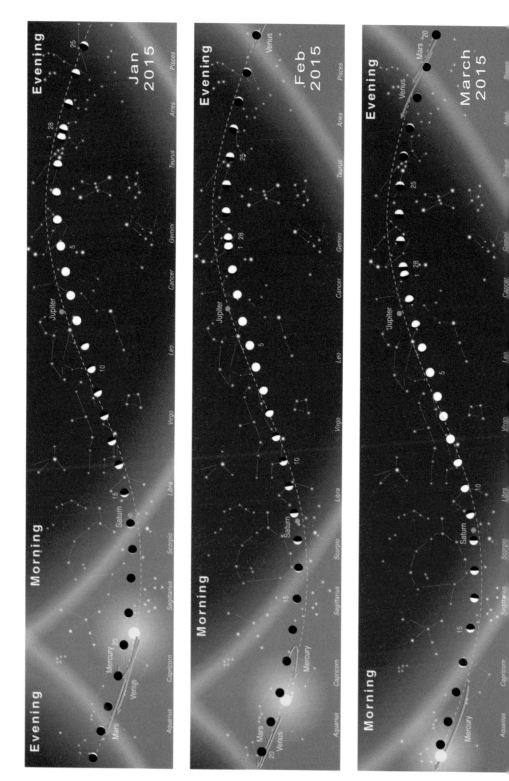

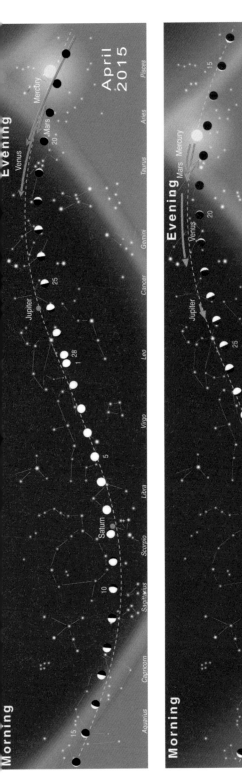
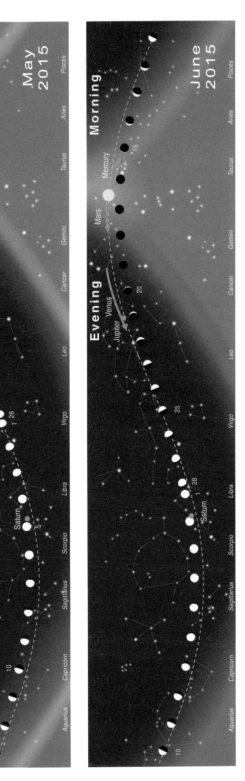

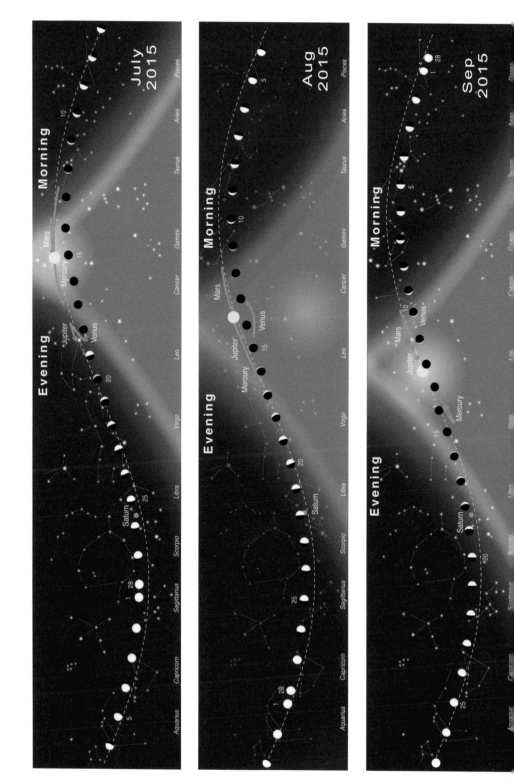

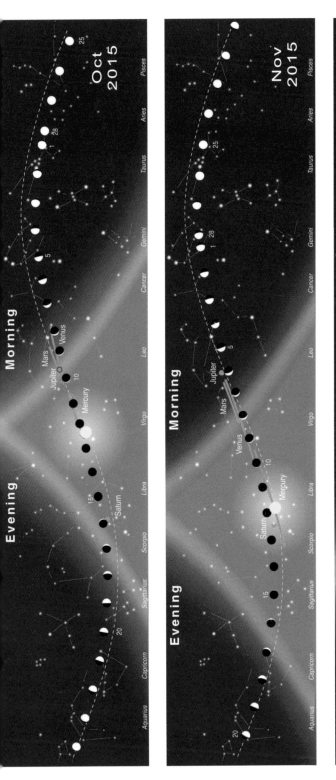

Further reading

Colquhoun, Margaret and Axel Ewald, *New Eyes for Plants,* Hawthorn.

Conford, Philip, *The Origins of the Organic Movement,* Floris.

—, *The Development of the Organic Network,* Floris.

Karlsson, Britt and Per, *Biodynamic, Organic and Natural Winemaking,* Floris.

Klett, Manfred, *Principles of Biodynamic Spray and Compost Preparations,* Floris.

Koepf, H.H. *The Biodynamic Farm,* Anthroposophic, USA.

—, *Koepf's Practical Biodynamics: Soil, Compost, Sprays and Food Quality,* Floris.

Kranich, Ernst Michael, *Planetary Influences upon Plants,* Biodynamic Literature, USA.

Lepetit, Anton, *What's so Special About Biodynamic Wine?* Floris.

Masson, Pierre, *A Biodynamic Manual,* Floris.

Osthaus, Karl-Ernst, *The Biodynamic Farm,* Floris.

Pfeiffer, Ehrenfried, *The Earth's Face,* Lanthorn.

—, *Pfeiffer's Introduction to Biodynamics,* Floris.

—, *Soil Fertility, Renewal and Preservation,* Lanthorn.

—, *Weeds and What They Tell Us,* Floris.

—, & Michael Maltas, *The Biodynamic Orchard Book,* Floris.

Philbrick, John and Helen, *Gardening for Health and Nutrition,* Anthroposophic Press, USA.

Sattler, Friedrich & Eckard von Wistinghausen, *Growing Biodynamic Crops,* Floris.

Schilthuis, Willy, *Biodynamic Agriculture,* Floris.

Soper, John, *Biodynamic Gardening,* Biodynamic Agricultural Ass. UK.

Steiner, Rudolf, *Agriculture (A Course of Eight Lectures),* Biodynamic Literature, USA.

—, *Agriculture: An Introductory Reader,* Steiner Press, UK.

—, *What is Biodynamics? A Way to Heal and Revitalize the Earth,* SteinerBooks, USA.

Storl, Wolf, *Culture and Horticulture,* Biodynamic Farming & Gardening Ass. USA.

Thun, Maria, *Gardening for Life,* Hawthorn.

—, *The Biodynamic Year,* Temple Lodge.

von Keyserlink, Adelbert Count, *The Birth of a New Agriculture,* Temple Lodge.

—, *Developing Biodynamic Agriculture,* Temple Lodge.

Waldin, Monty, *Monty Waldin's Best Biodynamic Wines,* Floris.

Weiler, Michael, *Bees and Honey, from Flower to Jar,* Floris.

Wright, Hilary, *Biodynamic Gardening for Health and Taste,* Floris.

Biodynamic Associations

Demeter International e.V.
www.demeter.net
Australia:
Bio-Dynamic Agricultural Assoc. of Australia
www.demeter.org.au
Biodynamic Agricultural Assoc.
www.biodynamics.net.au
Canada: Society for Bio-Dynamic Farming & Gardening in Ontario
www.biodynamics.on.ca
India: Bio-Dynamic Assoc. of India (BDAI)
www.biodynamics.in

Ireland: Biodynamic Agricultural Assoc.
www.biodynamic.ie
New Zealand:
Biodynamic Farming & Gardening Assoc.
www.biodynamic.org.nz
South Africa: Biodynamic Agricultural Assoc. of Southern Africa
www.bdaasa.org.za
UK: Biodynamic Agricultural Assoc. (BDAA)
www.biodynamic.org.uk
USA: Biodynamic Farming and Gardening Assoc.
www.biodynamics.com

amic Calendar 2015

2015

All times in GMT

:ed
10 11 12 13 14 15 16 17 18 19 20 21 22 23 24

Flower	
	Leaf from 13ʰ
Leaf	
	Fruit from 7ʰ
Fruit	
Fruit	
	Root from 6ʰ
	- - - - - - - - Rt 20ʰ
Root	
Root	
Flower from 2ʰ	
	Leaf from 13ʰ
Leaf	
to 19ʰ	Fruit 20ʰ
Fruit	
Jit to 21ʰ	22ʰ
Root	
ɔ 18ʰ	- - - - - - - -
- - - - - - - - - - - -	Fl 20ʰ
	Leaf from 10ʰ
	- - - - - - - - 19-21 - - -
af from 1ʰ to 23ʰ	
2ʰ	- - - - - - - - - - - - - - -
14ʰ	Leaf from 15ʰ
	Root from 6ʰ
	Flower from 13ʰ
Flower	

10 11 12 13 14 15 16 17 18 19 20 21 22 23 24

4 16ʰ and from Feb 27 13ʰ
20ʰ to Feb 27 6ʰ

March 2015

All times in GMT

Date	Const. of Moon	Parts of plant enhanced 0 1 2 3 4 5 6 7 8 9 10 11 12 13 14 15 16 17 18 19 20 21 22 23 24
1 Sun	♋ 19ʰ	Flower to 18ʰ — Leaf 19ʰ
2 Mon	♋	Leaf
3 Tue	♌ 13ʰ	Leaf to 19ʰ — Fruit 20ʰ
4 Wed	♌	Fruit to 7ʰ — Leaf from 8ʰ to 17ʰ — Fruit 18ʰ
5 Thu	♌	Fruit
6 Fri	♍ 12ʰ	Fruit to 11ʰ — Root from 12ʰ
7 Sat	♍	Root to 17ʰ - - - - - - - -

Northern Transplanting Time

DST begins in N America

Date	Const. of Moon	
8 Sun	♍	Root from 0ʰ
9 Mon	♍	Root to 17ʰ — Leaf from 18ʰ
10 Tue	♎ 9ʰ	Leaf to 9ʰ — Flower from 10ʰ
11 Wed	♏ 19ʰ	Flower to 18ʰ — Leaf 19ʰ
12 Thu	♏	Leaf
13 Fri	♏	Leaf
14 Sat	♐ 5ʰ	Lf to 4ʰ Fr 5-8ʰ - - - - - - - - - - - -

Southern Transplanting Time

Date	Const. of Moon	
15 Sun	♐	- -
16 Mon	♑ 8ʰ	- - - - - Fr 4-7ʰ — Root from 8ʰ
17 Tue	♑	Root
18 Wed	♒ 6ʰ	Root to 5ʰ — Flower from 6ʰ
19 Thu	♓ 22ʰ	Flower to 8ʰ - - - - - - - - - - - - - - -
20 Fri	♓	- - - - - - - - - - - Leaf from 12ʰ to 23ʰ
21 Sat	♓	- - - - - - - Lf 6 - 10ʰ - - - Leaf 14ʰ - 22ʰ
22 Sun	♈ 10ʰ	- - Leaf 2ʰ to 9ʰ — Fruit from 10ʰ
23 Mon	♈	Fruit
24 Tue	♉ 3ʰ	-2ʰ — Root from 3ʰ
25 Wed	♉	Root to 9ʰ — Leaf from 10ʰ to 23ʰ
26 Thu	♊ 19ʰ	Root from 0ʰ to 18ʰ — Flower 19ʰ
27 Fri	♊	Flower
28 Sat	♊	Flower to 24ʰ

N T T

DST begins in Europe

(incl UK). **All times below continue in GMT**

Date	Const. of Moon	
29 Sun	♋ 1ʰ	Leaf from 1ʰ to 24ʰ
30 Mon	♌ 20ʰ	Fruit from 1ʰ to 10ʰ — Leaf 11ʰ to 19ʰ — Fr 20ʰ
31 Tue	♌	Fruit

0 1 2 3 4 5 6 7 8 9 10 11 12 13 14 15 16 17 18 19 20 21 22 23 24

Northern Transplanting Time to March 14 1ʰ and from March 26 19ʰ
Southern Transplanting Time March 14 5ʰ to March 26 13ʰ

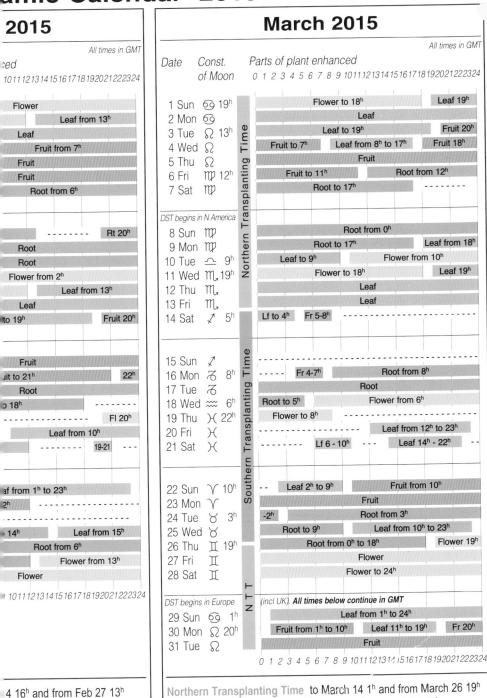

The Maria Thun Bioc

July 2015

All times in GMT

Date	Const. of Moon	Parts of plant enhanced
1 Wed	♐ 7ʰ	Leaf to 6ʰ / Fruit 7ʰ to 14ʰ / Flower from 15ʰ
2 Thu	♐	1ʰ / Fruit from 2ʰ
3 Fri	♑ 10ʰ	Fruit to 9ʰ / Root from 10ʰ to 20ʰ ----
4 Sat	♑	----
5 Sun	♒ 9ʰ	----
6 Mon	♒	Flower from 7ʰ
7 Tue	♓ 3ʰ	- 2ʰ / Leaf from 3ʰ to 22ʰ --
8 Wed	♓	---- Leaf 4ʰ to 10ʰ / Flower from 11ʰ to 24ʰ
9 Thu	♈ 20ʰ	---- Leaf from 5ʰ to 19ʰ / Fruit 20ʰ
10 Fri	♈	Fruit
11 Sat	♉ 13ʰ	Fruit -4ʰ ----
12 Sun	♉	---- Root from 16ʰ
13 Mon	♉	Root to 8ʰ / Flower from 9ʰ to 22ʰ / 23
14 Tue	♊ 6ʰ	Root to 5ʰ / Flower from 6ʰ
15 Wed	♊	Flower / Fruit & Flower 12ʰ to 24ʰ
16 Thu	♋ 10ʰ	Flower to 9ʰ / Leaf from 10ʰ
17 Fri	♋	Leaf
18 Sat	♌ 3ʰ	- 2ʰ / Fruit from 3ʰ to 22ʰ --
19 Sun	♌	--- / Fruit from 3ʰ
20 Mon	♌	Fruit to 24ʰ
21 Tue	♍ 1ʰ	1-3ʰ / Leaf 4ʰ-13ʰ / 14-16 -------- 23
22 Wed	♍	Root to 10ʰ / Leaf 11ʰ to 22ʰ / 23
23 Thu	♍	Root
24 Fri	♎ 22ʰ	Root to 21ʰ / 22ʰ
25 Sat	♎	Flower
26 Sun	♏ 8ʰ	Flower to 7ʰ / Leaf from 8ʰ
27 Mon	♏	Leaf
28 Tue	♐ 17ʰ	Leaf to 16ʰ / Fruit from 17ʰ
29 Wed	♐	Fruit
30 Thu	♑ 20ʰ	Fruit to 19ʰ / Root 20ʰ
31 Fri	♑	Root

0 1 2 3 4 5 6 7 8 9 10 11 12 13 14 15 16 17 18 19 20 21 22 23 24

Southern Transplanting Time (July 1 – July 11)

Northern Transplanting Time (July 12 – July 25)

Southern Transplanting Time (S T T, July 28 onward)

In UK/Ireland remember to add 1 hour for Daylight Saving Time

Northern Transplanting Time to July 1 6ʰ and July 14 6ʰ to July 28 16ʰ
Southern Transplanting Time July 1 8ʰ to July 14 3ʰ and from July 28 19ʰ

Aug

Date	Const. of Moon	Parts of pla
1 Sat	♒ 17ʰ	
2 Sun	♒	----
3 Mon	♓ 10ʰ	Flower
4 Tue	♓	----
5 Wed	♓	Leaf to
6 Thu	♈ 1ʰ	Le
7 Fri	♉ 19ʰ	
8 Sat	♉	
9 Sun	♉	
10 Mon	♊ 12ʰ	Roo
11 Tue	♊	
12 Wed	♋ 17ʰ	
13 Thu	♋	
14 Fri	♌ 10ʰ	Leaf t
15 Sat	♌	
16 Sun	♌	
17 Mon	♍ 8ʰ	Fruit to 7
18 Tue	♍	--- Fl 3-
19 Wed	♍	----
20 Thu	♍	
21 Fri	♎ 5ʰ	Rt -4ʰ
22 Sat	♏ 17ʰ	
23 Sun	♏	
24 Mon	♏	
25 Tue	♐ 2ʰ	1ʰ
26 Wed	♐	
27 Thu	♑ 6ʰ	Fr to 5ʰ
28 Fri	♑	
29 Sat	♒ 4ʰ	Rt -3ʰ
30 Sun	♓ 20ʰ	Fl to 4ʰ
31 Mon	♓	----

S T T (Southern Transplanting Time)

Northern Transplanting Time (August)

Southern Transplanting Time

Northern Transplanting Time
Southern Transplanting Time

October 2015

All times in GMT

Date	Const. of Moon	Parts of plant enhanced (0–24h)	Transplanting time
1 Thu	♉ 10^h	Fruit to 9^h; Root from 10^h	Southern
2 Fri	♉	Root	Southern
3 Sat	♉	Root to 23^h	Southern
DST begins in Australia			
4 Sun	♊ 0^h	Flower from 0^h	Northern
5 Mon	♊	Flower	Northern
6 Tue	♋ 4^h	Fl -3^h; Leaf from 4^h	Northern
7 Wed	♌ 21^h	-2^h - - - - -	Northern
8 Thu	♌	- - - - - Fr 21^h	Northern
9 Fri	♌	Fruit	Northern
10 Sat	♍ 20^h	Fruit to 19^h; Root 20^h	Northern
11 Sun	♍	Root to 5^h - - - - - Fruit from 14^h	Northern
12 Mon	♍	Fr -3^h; Root from 4^h	Northern
13 Tue	♍	Root	Northern
14 Wed	♎ 17^h	Root to 16^h; Flower 17^h	Northern
15 Thu	♎	Flower to 15^h; Fruit from 16^h	Northern
16 Fri	♏ 5^h	Fruit to 7^h; Leaf from 8^h	Northern
17 Sat	♏	Leaf	Northern
18 Sun	♐ 17^h	Leaf to 16^h; Fruit from 17^h	Northern / Southern
19 Mon	♐	Fruit	Southern
20 Tue	♐	Fruit to 23^h	Southern
21 Wed	♑ 0^h	Root from 0^h	Southern
22 Thu	♑	Root to 23^h	Southern
23 Fri	♒ 0^h	Fruit from 0^h to 11^h; Flower from 12^h	Southern
24 Sat	♓ 17^h	Flower to 16^h; Leaf from 17^h	Southern
DST ends in Europe		*(incl UK and Ireland)*	
25 Sun	♓	1^h - - - - -	Southern
26 Mon	♓	- - - - -	Southern
27 Tue	♈ 6^h	Lf 1^h - 5^h; Fruit from 6^h	Southern
28 Wed	♉ 20^h	Fruit to 19^h; Root 20^h	Southern
29 Thu	♉	Root	Southern
30 Fri	♉	Root	Southern
31 Sat	♊ 9^h	Root to 8^h; Flower from 9^h	Southern / Northern
DST ends in North America			

Northern Transplanting Time Oct 4 0^h to Oct 18 17^h and from Oct 31 10^h
Southern Transplanting Time to Oct 3 22^h and Oct 18 20^h to Oct 31 6^h

Nov

Date	Const. of Moon	Parts of p… (0 1 2 3 4)	Transplanting time
1 Sun	♊		Northern
2 Mon	♋ 12^h	Flo…	Northern
3 Tue	♋		Northern
4 Wed	♌ 4^h	Lf -3^h	Northern
5 Thu	♌		Northern
6 Fri	♌		Northern
7 Sat	♍ 3^h	-2^h F…	Northern
8 Sun	♍	1^h	Northern
9 Mon	♍		Northern
10 Tue	♍		Northern
11 Wed	♎ 0^h		Northern
12 Thu	♏ 11^h	Flow…	Northern
13 Fri	♏		Northern
14 Sat	♐ 22^h	L…	Northern
15 Sun	♐	- - - - -	
16 Mon	♐		Southern
17 Tue	♑ 5^h	Fr -4^h	Southern
18 Wed	♑		Southern
19 Thu	♒ 7^h	Root to	Southern
20 Fri	♒		Southern
21 Sat	♓ 2^h	1^h Le…	Southern
22 Sun	♓		Southern
23 Mon	♈ 16^h	Leaf …	Southern
24 Tue	♈	- - - - -	Southern
25 Wed	♉ 7^h	Fruit to	Southern
26 Thu	♉		Southern
27 Fri	♊ 19^h		Southern
28 Sat	♊		N T T
29 Sun	♋ 21^h		N T T
30 Mon	♋		N T T

Northern Transplanting Tim…
Southern Transplanting Tim…

This poster is part of *The Maria Thun Biodynamic Cale…*

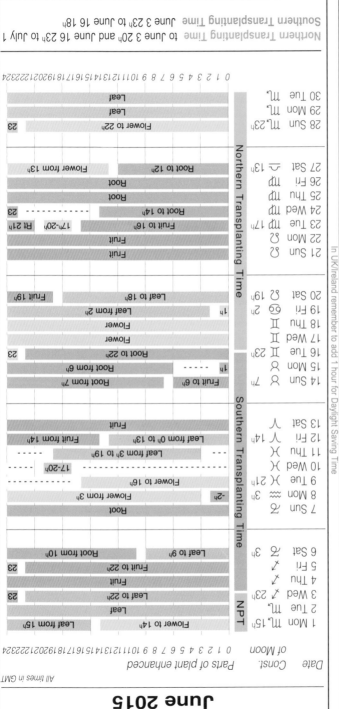

June 2015

All times in GMT

Date / Const. of Moon — Parts of plant enhanced

Northern Transplanting Time to June 3 20^h and June 16 23^h to July 1

Southern Transplanting Time June 3 23^h to June 16 18^h

In UK/Ireland remember to add 1 hour for Daylight Saving Time

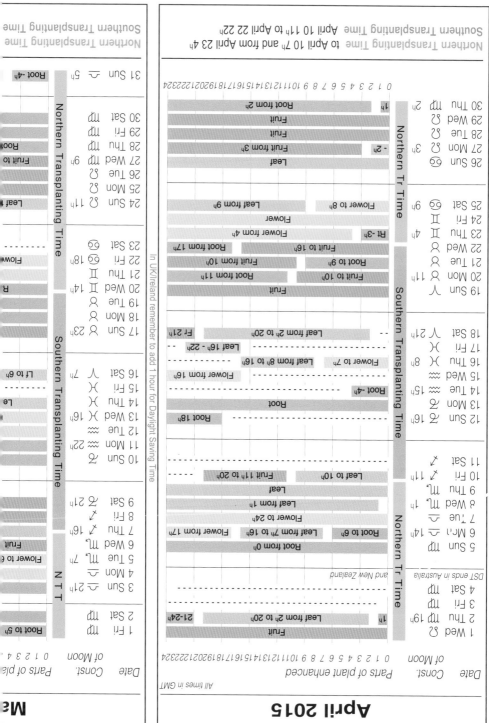

December 2015

All times in GMT

Northern Transplanting Time ___ to Dec 12 7ʰ and Dec 25 9ʰ to Jan 8
Southern Transplanting Time Dec 12 10ʰ to Dec 25 6ʰ

Date	Const.	Parts of plant enhanced	Const	of Moon
1 Tue	♌ 13ʰ	Leaf to 17ʰ, Fruit 18ʰ	N T T	
2 Wed	♌	Fruit		
3 Thu	♌	Fruit		
4 Fri	♍ 10ʰ	Rt 10ʰ-15ʰ, 23, Fruit to 9ʰ		
5 Sat	♍	Root to 5ʰ, Flower from 6ʰ to 18ʰ, Root 19ʰ		
6 Sun	♍	Root from 5ʰ		
7 Mon	♍			
8 Tue	♎ 8ʰ	Root to 16ʰ, Root 20ʰ, Flower 8ʰ to 16ʰ, Leaf from 17ʰ, Root 7ʰ		
9 Wed	♏ 18ʰ	Leaf (very good)		
10 Thu	♏	Leaf		
11 Fri	♏	Leaf		
12 Sat	♐ 5ʰ	Lf to 4ʰ, Fruit from 5ʰ		
13 Sun	♐	Fruit	Southern Transplanting Time	
14 Mon	♑ 11ʰ	Root from 11ʰ, Fruit to 10ʰ		
15 Tue	♒	Root		
16 Wed	♒ 12ʰ	Root to 11ʰ, Flower from 12ʰ		
17 Thu	♒	Flower		
18 Fri	♓ 8ʰ	Fl to 7ʰ, Lf 8ʰ-12ʰ, Leaf 20ʰ		
19 Sat	♓	Leaf to 24ʰ		
20 Sun	♓	Leaf from 4ʰ to 21ʰ		
21 Mon	♈ 0ʰ	Fr 21ʰ		
22 Tue	♉ 16ʰ	Fruit to 15ʰ, Root from 16ʰ		
23 Wed	♉	Root		
24 Thu	♉	Root		
25 Fri	♊ 5ʰ	Root -4ʰ, 5-7ʰ, Fruit from 8ʰ to 23ʰ, Flower from 0ʰ		
26 Sat	♊	Flower from 0ʰ		
27 Sun	♋ 7ʰ	Flower to 7ʰ, Leaf from 7ʰ	N T T	
28 Mon	♋ 22ʰ	Leaf to 21ʰ, 22ʰ		
29 Tue	♋	Fruit		
30 Wed	♋	Fruit		
31 Thu	♍ 18ʰ	Fruit to 17ʰ		

0 1 2 3 4 5 6 7 8 9 10 11 12 13 14 15 16 17 18 19 20 21 22 23 24

2015

All times in GMT

14 12ʰ and from Nov 27 21ʰ
22ʰ to Nov 27 19ʰ

Flower		
Leaf from 12ʰ		
Leaf		
Fruit from 4ʰ		
Fruit		
Fruit		
Flower 19ʰ	... to 12ʰ	
Leaf from 11ʰ		
Root to 23ʰ	Flower from 0ʰ	
Root from 2ʰ	Root	
Fruit	22ʰ	
Root from 5ʰ	Root	
Flower from 7ʰ		
Flower		
Leaf 19ʰ		
17ʰ	Lf 21ʰ	
Fruit from 8ʰ		
Root from 7ʰ		
Root		
Flower 19ʰ	to 18ʰ	
Flower		
Lt 21ʰ	er to 20ʰ	
Leaf		

10 11 12 13 14 15 16 17 18 19 20 21 22 23 24

amic Calendar 2015

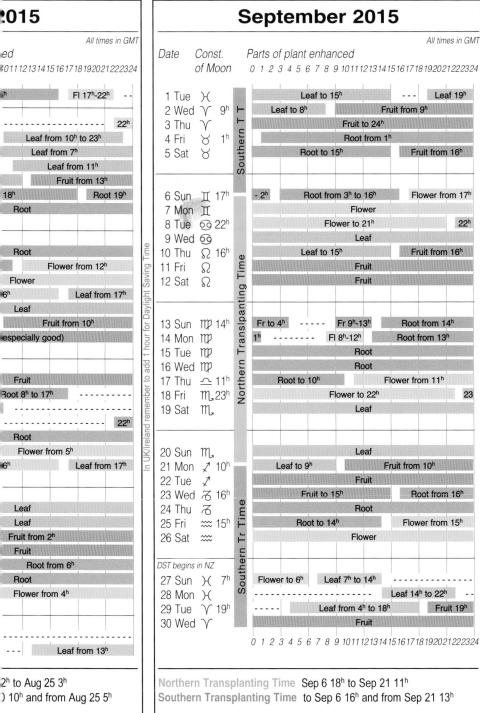

2015

All times in GMT

`10 11 12 13 14 15 16 17 18 19 20 21 22 23 24`

- Fl 17ʰ-22ʰ - -
- 22ʰ
- Leaf from 10ʰ to 23ʰ
- Leaf from 7ʰ
- Leaf from 11ʰ
- Fruit from 13ʰ
- 18ʰ   Root 19ʰ
- Root

- Root
- Flower from 12ʰ
- Flower
- 6ʰ   Leaf from 17ʰ
- Leaf
- Fruit from 10ʰ
- (especially good)

- Fruit
- Root 8ʰ to 17ʰ - - - - - - - - -
- -
- 22ʰ
- Root
- Flower from 5ʰ
- 6ʰ   Leaf from 17ʰ

- Leaf
- Leaf
- Fruit from 2ʰ
- Fruit
- Root from 6ʰ
- Root
- Flower from 4ʰ

- -
- - -   Leaf from 13ʰ

2ʰ to Aug 25 3ʰ
) 10ʰ and from Aug 25 5ʰ

September 2015

All times in GMT

Date	Const. of Moon	Parts of plant enhanced

`0 1 2 3 4 5 6 7 8 9 10 11 12 13 14 15 16 17 18 19 20 21 22 23 24`

Southern Tr T

- 1 Tue ♓ — Leaf to 15ʰ - - - Leaf 19ʰ
- 2 Wed ♈ 9ʰ — Leaf to 8ʰ   Fruit from 9ʰ
- 3 Thu ♈ — Fruit to 24ʰ
- 4 Fri ♉ 1ʰ — Root from 1ʰ
- 5 Sat ♉ — Root to 15ʰ   Fruit from 16ʰ

Northern Transplanting Time

- 6 Sun ♊ 17ʰ — - 2ʰ   Root from 3ʰ to 16ʰ   Flower from 17ʰ
- 7 Mon ♊ — Flower
- 8 Tue ♋ 22ʰ — Flower to 21ʰ   22ʰ
- 9 Wed ♋ — Leaf
- 10 Thu ♌ 16ʰ — Leaf to 15ʰ   Fruit from 16ʰ
- 11 Fri ♌ — Fruit
- 12 Sat ♌ — Fruit

- 13 Sun ♍ 14ʰ — Fr to 4ʰ - - - - - Fr 9ʰ-13ʰ   Root from 14ʰ
- 14 Mon ♍ — 1ʰ - - - - - - - - Fl 8ʰ-12ʰ   Root from 13ʰ
- 15 Tue ♍ — Root
- 16 Wed ♍ — Root
- 17 Thu ♎ 11ʰ — Root to 10ʰ   Flower from 11ʰ
- 18 Fri ♏ 23ʰ — Flower to 22ʰ   23
- 19 Sat ♏ — Leaf

Southern Tr Time

- 20 Sun ♏ — Leaf
- 21 Mon ♐ 10ʰ — Leaf to 9ʰ   Fruit from 10ʰ
- 22 Tue ♐ — Fruit
- 23 Wed ♑ 16ʰ — Fruit to 15ʰ   Root from 16ʰ
- 24 Thu ♑ — Root
- 25 Fri ♒ 15ʰ — Root to 14ʰ   Flower from 15ʰ
- 26 Sat ♒ — Flower

DST begins in NZ

- 27 Sun ♓ 7ʰ — Flower to 6ʰ   Leaf 7ʰ to 14ʰ - - - - - - - - - - - - - - - -
- 28 Mon ♓ — -   Leaf 14ʰ to 22ʰ - -
- 29 Tue ♈ 19ʰ — - - - - -   Leaf from 4ʰ to 18ʰ   Fruit 19ʰ
- 30 Wed ♈ — Fruit

`0 1 2 3 4 5 6 7 8 9 10 11 12 13 14 15 16 17 18 19 20 21 22 23 24`

In UK/Ireland remember to add 1 hour for Daylight Saving Time

Northern Transplanting Time Sep 6 18ʰ to Sep 21 11ʰ
Southern Transplanting Time to Sep 6 16ʰ and from Sep 21 13ʰ

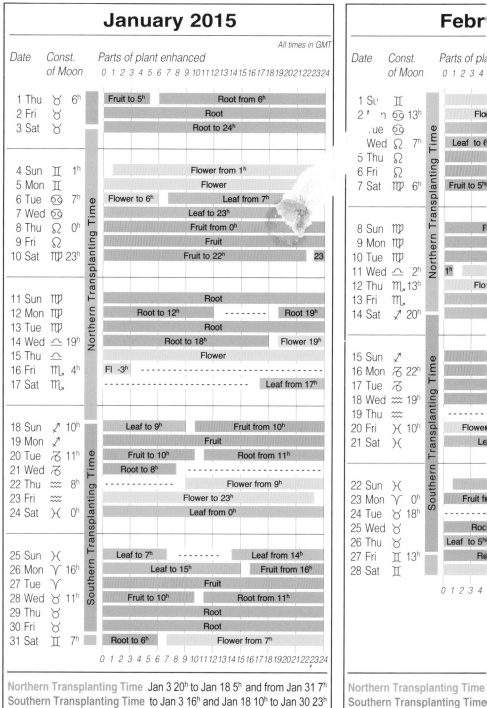

January 2015

All times in GMT

Date	Const. of Moon	Parts of plant enhanced
1 Thu	♉ 6ʰ	Fruit to 5ʰ / Root from 6ʰ
2 Fri	♉	Root
3 Sat	♉	Root to 24ʰ
4 Sun	♊ 1ʰ	Flower from 1ʰ
5 Mon	♊	Flower
6 Tue	♋ 7ʰ	Flower to 6ʰ / Leaf from 7ʰ
7 Wed	♋	Leaf to 23ʰ
8 Thu	♌ 0ʰ	Fruit from 0ʰ
9 Fri	♌	Fruit
10 Sat	♍ 23ʰ	Fruit to 22ʰ 23
11 Sun	♍	Root
12 Mon	♍	Root to 12ʰ ------ Root 19ʰ
13 Tue	♍	Root
14 Wed	♎ 19ʰ	Root to 18ʰ / Flower 19ʰ
15 Thu	♎	Flower
16 Fri	♏ 4ʰ	Fl -3ʰ -------------
17 Sat	♏	------------- Leaf from 17ʰ
18 Sun	♐ 10ʰ	Leaf to 9ʰ / Fruit from 10ʰ
19 Mon	♐	Fruit
20 Tue	♑ 11ʰ	Fruit to 10ʰ / Root from 11ʰ
21 Wed	♑	Root to 8ʰ --------------
22 Thu	♒ 8ʰ	-------------- Flower from 9ʰ
23 Fri	♒	Flower to 23ʰ
24 Sat	♓ 0ʰ	Leaf from 0ʰ
25 Sun	♓	Leaf to 7ʰ ------ Leaf from 14ʰ
26 Mon	♈ 16ʰ	Leaf to 15ʰ / Fruit from 16ʰ
27 Tue	♈	Fruit
28 Wed	♉ 11ʰ	Fruit to 10ʰ / Root from 11ʰ
29 Thu	♉	Root
30 Fri	♉	Root
31 Sat	♊ 7ʰ	Root to 6ʰ / Flower from 7ʰ

Northern Transplanting Time (Jan 3 20ʰ to Jan 18 5ʰ and from Jan 31 7ʰ)

Southern Transplanting Time (to Jan 3 16ʰ and Jan 18 10ʰ to Jan 30 23ʰ)

0 1 2 3 4 5 6 7 8 9 10 11 12 13 14 15 16 17 18 19 20 21 22 23 24

Northern Transplanting Time Jan 3 20ʰ to Jan 18 5ʰ and from Jan 31 7ʰ
Southern Transplanting Time to Jan 3 16ʰ and Jan 18 10ʰ to Jan 30 23ʰ

Febr

Date	Const. of Moon	Parts of pla
1 Su	♊	
2	♋ 13ʰ	Flo
3 ue	♋	
4 Wed	♌ 7ʰ	Leaf to 6
5 Thu	♌	
6 Fri	♌	
7 Sat	♍ 6ʰ	Fruit to 5ʰ
8 Sun	♍	F
9 Mon	♍	
10 Tue	♍	
11 Wed	♎ 2ʰ	1ʰ
12 Thu	♏ 13ʰ	Flo
13 Fri	♏	
14 Sat	♐ 20ʰ	
15 Sun	♐	
16 Mon	♑ 22ʰ	
17 Tue	♑	
18 Wed	♒ 19ʰ	
19 Thu	♒	------
20 Fri	♓ 10ʰ	Flower
21 Sat	♓	Le
22 Sun	♓	
23 Mon	♈ 0ʰ	Fruit fr
24 Tue	♉ 18ʰ	------
25 Wed	♉	Roc
26 Thu	♉	Leaf to 5ʰ
27 Fri	♊ 13ʰ	Re
28 Sat	♊	

0 1 2 3 4

Northern Transplanting Time
Southern Transplanting Time